The Human Heredity Handbook

ALSO BY AMRAM SCHEINFELD
You and Heredity (1939)
Women and Men (1944)
The New You and Heredity (1950)

The
Human Heredity
Handbook

BY AMRAM SCHEINFELD

ILLUSTRATED BY THE AUTHOR

J. B. LIPPINCOTT COMPANY

PHILADELPHIA AND NEW YORK

To my beloved wife
Dorothy

Preface

This book seeks to bring to the reader all the important facts about human heredity which science has so far discovered, and to present these facts as clearly, accurately, interestingly—and, in particular—as *concisely* as possible.

While the Handbook has drawn liberally on its big, senior brother, *"The New* You and Heredity," for a considerable amount of its material, I should make clear that it is in no sense an adaptation or abridgement. In format, style and language, in much of its data, and in most of its illustrations which I have drawn, "The Human Heredity Handbook" is a new work. Nor does there have to be any serious sibling rivalry between these two books of mine. Rather, it is my thought that they will prove to be worthy and helpful adjuncts to one another.

In other words, the Handbook has been planned by my publishers and myself to serve a new and growing need for a quick, handy, untechnical, practical (and economical) guide to the general subject of human inheritance, and to provide direct, uncomplicated answers to such specific questions on the subject as may be asked by parents and prospective parents, teachers, students, medical men, marriage counselors, and other interested persons.

Should the reader desire more detailed information on many points dealt with, and some not covered in the Handbook, or wish to have sources of the data and suggestions for further study, he is respectfully referred to the much more comprehensive work, *"The New* You and Heredity." Contrariwise, those who own the latter volume may find that the Handbook is a useful supplement for quick reference, and offers considerable additional information, especially on the most recent findings and developments in the fields covered.

PREFACE

Although conciseness has been a principal objective in preparing the Handbook, there has been no less stress on achieving accuracy as well. To that end much valuable aid, which I gratefully acknowledge, was given by my friend, Dr. C. Nash Herndon, Professor of Medical Genetics, Bowman Gray School of Medicine, who read the complete manuscript and made many important suggestions for its improvement. I also owe thanks to these other good friends: Professor Irving Lorge, of Teachers College, Columbia University, and Professor David Wechsler, New York University, for helpful comments on the discussions of "Intelligence" and "Talents" in Chapters 19 and 20; Dr. Alexander Wiener, for his aid with the discussions of blood types and conditions in Chapters 15, 26 and 28; and Professor Morris Harnly, New York University, for checking my "Glossary" (*Appendix*). Any remaining errors or sins of omission or commission in this book, I can ascribe only to myself.

Finally, I am grateful to another good friend, Ernst Reichl, for his skillful and talented aid in styling the jacket and typography of this book, and to my publishers, J. B. Lippincott Company, for helping to bring it into being. To conform to the copyright laws, I also hereby formally thank myself and my publishers for permission to use or adapt a number of illustrations from "*The New* You and Heredity." Specific acknowledgments are appended wherever these illustrations appear.

AMRAM SCHEINFELD

New York City
February 1, 1956

Contents

List of Illustrations

LIST OF ILLUSTRATIONS

The Human Heredity Handbook

Human Chromosomes

As they look (after staining) under the microscope.
Magnification about 1,500 times

1. The 48 chromosomes in the stretched-out stage. (Some of the chromosomes in this picture, and the one below, are hidden by others, so the full 48 cannot be counted.)

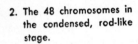
2. The 48 chromosomes in the condensed, rod-like stage.

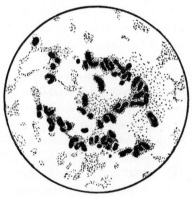

3. Diagram of a greatly magnified chromosome section, showing the beads or segments which contain the genes.

(Figures 1 and 2 are adapted from actual photographs reproduced in *The New* YOU AND HEREDITY. Copyright, 1950, by Amram Scheinfeld.)

I

Heredity
and Environment

WHY THIS BOOK? We hear people say, "I don't believe in heredity—I believe in environment." Or, "I think environment is more important than heredity." Others say, "That whole family is just no good—drunks, criminals, paupers—it's because they've got rotten heredity." Or, "Some groups are born to be superior, other groups to be inferior, and the quickest way to improve humanity is to breed out the inferior people." All such statements are based on wrong ideas as to what heredity means, how it works, and what part it does or does not play in people's lives. These misconceptions have caused much suffering, injustice, confusion and unhappiness from the beginning of mankind's history. But at last, after decades of intensive study, the science of *genetics,* which deals with heredity, has cleared the air to a vast extent and has provided many positive, accurate answers in place of previous myths and fallacies. This book, then, will try to present the facts about human heredity as scientists now know them, and to indicate how you, the reader, can usefully apply these facts to increase your understanding of yourself, your children and your fellow men.

WHAT IS "HEREDITY?" First, it is what makes us what we are as members of a particular species—in our case, human beings. When a woman is pregnant, we know definitely that she is not going to give birth to a little elephant, kangaroo, mouse or bird, but to a *human* baby. We know that this child will have a *human* nose, not a snout or beak; *human* hands and feet, not hoofs or claws; a *human* brain, heart, lungs, skin, etc. In countless details, then, it is heredity that causes human beings to produce offspring who are like themselves and like no other living things, just as it is heredity that causes all other creatures

3

—dogs, cats, chickens, fish, apes, etc.—to produce offspring of their own kind. Further, heredity has much to do with producing the resemblances between individual parents and their offspring, and among members of the same family groups, in numerous physical and mental traits.

WHAT ABOUT "ENVIRONMENT"? That, too, is extremely important in making people what they are. By "environment" we mean everything *outside* the individual and his inherited factors, from conception on. Before birth the environment is the mother's womb, the nourishment she supplies to the embryo baby, and all the conditions under which he or she develops. After the baby is born, the environment includes not only what he is fed and how he is cared for, but everything he sees, hears and is able to learn. As the child grows, his upbringing, surroundings, emotional life, hygienic conditions, medical care, experiences, playmates, schooling, attitudes of others—all these are increasingly important parts of his environment. No matter how good a child's heredity, a very bad environment may ruin his chances of becoming a healthy, useful, well-adjusted person. Equally, no matter how good the environment, a child with very bad or defective heredity may not be able to survive, or to develop normally and successfully.

"HEREDITY VERSUS ENVIRONMENT." From what has been said, it should be clear that heredity and environment are not opposing forces, working always against one another. Rather, they are complementary forces, always working together. Every human being and every other living thing are products of both heredity and environment. Without both there could be no life, nor any particular type of creature. Everything you are, and everything anyone can be made to be, depends always on the *potentialities* of heredity, working together with the *possibilities* of environment. Very good heredity can often offset some of the disadvantages of poor environment, as has been proved in the cases of Abraham Lincoln, George Washington Carver and many other great people who worked their way to the top against heavy odds. And very good environment can often help to make up for some of the lacks of heredity. For instance, kindly and expert training can cause a child born with inherited blindness, or some crippling condition, to become a happy and well-adjusted person. Fortunately, *most* human beings are born with pretty good heredity, and more and more persons today are growing up in good environments.

▶ *"Which is more important—heredity or environment?"* This once-popular subject for school debates or informal arguments now arouses only an indulgent smile from the scientist, who knows that the question as posed has no meaning. One can only ask it with respect to *particular* aspects or traits of inheritance. As stated before, both heredity and environment are essential to produce and sustain any living thing. So in general terms, neither force can be called "more important" than the other. However, in a garden the very same environment produces many species of flowers and vegetables, depending on which *seeds* were planted. Thus, in producing any particular kind of flower or vegetable, heredity can be called far more important than environment. Likewise, from the same prenatal environment in a mother may come two non-identical twins—one a girl, one a boy; one blue-eyed, one black-eyed; one normal-sighted, one color blind. In producing these differences between the children (including their sex), heredity is again vastly more important than their environment. But if a baby is born with a serious defect purely because of a prenatal accident, or some dietary deficiency, obviously in that case environment is the all-important factor. As we proceed with this book, and take up particular traits of numerous kinds, we will see every degree of both hereditary and environmental influence at work.

2

The New Baby

LIFE BEGINS. The conception of a new baby takes place the instant a sperm from the father enters and fertilizes an egg waiting in the mother. Usually one egg every four weeks is produced by a woman (although sometimes two or more are produced, which may give rise to twins, triplets, etc.). The egg comes out of either of the two ovaries and moves down into one of the two fallopian tubes. Here the egg is ready to be fertilized.

▶ *Fertilization.* In the act of intercourse the husband propels into the wife's vagina many millions of sperms (from 50,000,000 to 500,000,000 in an average single ejaculation). These sperms are so small millions could be packed into a pinhead. Like the tiniest imaginable tadpoles, they swim first in the stream of seminal fluid, then in the secretions of the vagina and womb. Only a small proportion get into the womb, and fewer still into the tubes. But should any sperms reach the egg, the moment a single one enters there is an instantaneous toughening of the covering of the egg which shuts out all other sperms. Thus, of all the millions of sperms entering the race, only a single one can win out and fertilize the egg.

THE HEREDITY ELEMENTS. If we could look through a powerful microscope and follow the process of conception, we would see this: As the sperm enters the egg, leaving its tail outside, the sperm-head opens and out comes a batch of twenty-four tiny little worm-like bits of living substance. At the same time a little globule inside the egg (the *nucleus*) also opens up, and out comes another batch of twenty-four of the same tiny little worm-like things. These little things in both the sperm and the egg are called "*chromosomes.*" They carry *everything a child inherits* from the parents. (See illustration, p. 2.)

6

▶ *The chromosomes.* As we examine them more closely, we find that among the chromosomes in each set—whether the twenty-four from the father or the twenty-four from the mother —one may differ from another in shape and size. But there is a more remarkable fact. Every chromosome from the father finds an exactly matching type, of its same shape and size, among the chromosomes waiting in the mother's egg. (An exception, in the "sex" chromosomes, will be explained in Chapter 4.) How the chromosomes look if those from the two parents are arranged in pairs is shown in our accompanying illustration.

How the Chromosomes Are Paired

Chromosomes
from Mother

Chromosomes
from Father

A B C D E F G H I J K L M N O P Q R S T U V W X Y

Note that except for the father's "sex" chromosome, which may be either an "X" or a "Y" (see Chap. 4), the chromosomes of each pair, whether from father or mother, are the same in size and structure (although they may differ in the nature of their genes). The letters assigned to the chromosomes here are merely for identification.

▶ *The genes.* Most often, when chromosomes are seen under a microscope, they are in a compressed form (which gives them their worm-like appearance). But at certain stages they stretch out, and then we find that each chromosome actually consists of hundreds of clear, jelly-like particles, strung together like beads. These beads are called *"genes"* (pronounced "jeans"). And it is these genes which act like wonderful little chemical workers to carry out the processes of heredity. Every gene differs from the others in some way, and has some special job to do in the fashioning and developing of a baby, from conception to birth. But even after birth, and throughout life, the genes continue their work.

THE STREAM OF HEREDITY. *"Acquired Characteristics."* One of the most important aspects of heredity is this: The genes as they pass along from generation to generation *are not changed in their workings* by any changes parents make in their own traits, or that are made in their traits by environment. Establishment of this fact has upset the old theory of the *inheritance of acquired characteristics*—that traits acquired by persons during their lifetimes, or environmental changes made in them, could indeed be transmitted to their offspring. The theory has been disproved by many experiments. Even before the science of genetics came into being, skeptical scientists had taken note of the fact that generations of binding of feet among Chinese, circumcision among Jews, mutilations among primitive peoples (enlarging lips, scarring faces, tattooing, etc.), had in no way produced any corresponding changes in their newborn offspring. Leaving no further doubts, scientists have since made countless experiments with lower animals—altering parts of their bodies, feeding them different diets and chemicals, training them in various ways for many generations—without in any way changing hereditary traits. (Sensational claims by the Soviet biologist, Lysenko, that he had "proved" the acquired-characteristics theory correct appear now to be discredited even in his own country. See Chap. 25.) How and why the genes retain their identity can now be best understood by looking into the processes through which eggs and sperms are formed.

▶ *Human egg production.* When a little girl baby is born, she already has in her tiny ovaries all the eggs—in rudimentary form—which will take mature shape and emerge after she achieves puberty. And within each rudimentary egg there already are present exact replicas of all the chromosomes and genes which the girl baby received from her parents at conception, and from which will be drawn all the chromosomes her own children will receive. An immediate question, then, is this: In what possible way could the genes so tightly enclosed in the eggs (whether rudimentary or mature) suddenly be made to change in conformity with anything or everything happening to the female in whose ovaries they are? It is obviously ridiculous to think that if a dark-haired girl bleached her hair blond, that would make her "dark-hair" genes suddenly turn into "blond" genes. Or if she got her straight hair permanently waved, that would cause her "straight-hair" genes to change suddenly so that her baby would be born with wavy hair. But it is no less ridiculous to assume that whenever a mother, or future mother, makes a change in any other trait of her body, mind or character (or any such change is made in her), the results will immediately cause the genes concerned with that trait to change their workings in conformity with the new requirements.

Human Sperms and Egg

Egg
nucleus

HUMAN SPERMS
Magnified as here shown about 400 times. (Actual size of sperm is about 1/400 of an inch long.)

HUMAN EGG
Relative size shown by sperm entering it. The egg nucleus contains the chromosomes. The rest is food material.

(Adapted from actual photographs in the author's book, The New YOU AND HEREDITY. Copyright, 1950, by Amram Scheinfeld.)

▶ *Human sperm production.* As with a little girl baby, a boy baby, too, when he is born already has set aside within him all the "germ cells" from which will some day come his contributions to his children's heredity. A difference between the sexes is that while in the female the eggs themselves are already present at birth, in the male the sperms do not begin to be fashioned by the germ cells until he achieves puberty. Another difference is that while the eggs of the female are limited in number (because she will usually produce no more than one a month for a period of about thirty years), the sperm production of the male, once it begins, goes on into the billions and billions, often throughout his lifetime. But except for the difference in numbers, the sperms of a male are the same as the eggs of a female with respect to the nature of their genes. In the male, too, all the genes carried in his sperms are exact replicas of those which he received from his parents at conception, and cannot be changed in their workings by any changes that are made in his own traits. (*Note:* How some changes, or "mutations," do occur in genes in rare instances will be explained in the next chapter, and later under "The First Life-Spark," Chapter 25. These gene changes are different from those we have discussed, and give no support to the "acquired-characteristic" theory.)

MOTHER AND CHILD. Although a child's genes can in no way be changed by the parents' acts, habits or experiences, this hardly means that a child's *traits* will not be affected by these influences. Obviously, parents can affect their child environmentally in a great many ways, from birth onward; and in the mother's case, her influences on the child's body and mind may begin from the moment of conception. However, there has been much confusion regarding the extent to which the mother's condition is responsible for various traits appearing in babies. Often conditions which are blamed on prenatal factors are due to heredity, and at other times the reverse is true.

▶ *Prenatal relationships.* The developing baby is in no sense ever a part of the mother's body. Though growing within her, the baby is always a distinct individual (as courts have ruled). Biologically there is a wall—the *placenta*—between the mother and baby. The mother's blood, which carries the nourishment, stops on one side of the wall and the blood elements are broken down and strained through it. There is therefore no more *direct blood tie* between a mother and child than between a father and child. The baby manufactures its own blood according to the formula prescribed by its "blood" genes. In fact, the baby's blood may be so different chemically from the mother's—for instance, with respect to the "Rh factor"—that an interchange of blood substances may sometimes cause serious damage. (Chap. 15.) Other hazards to the unborn baby: *Germs,* if the mother has any germ disease; *alcohol,* if the mother is a heavy drinker; *drugs,* if the mother is an addict; abnormal *hormonal or chemical states* in the mother; *dietary deficiencies.* Any of these factors— which, fortunately, occur in only a minority of the cases—may disturb the normal development of a baby, and produce various congenital diseases, defects or abnormalities which may be mistakenly regarded as hereditary. (More on these points in Chapters 3, 11, 13-17.)

▶ *Prenatal "impressions."* The basis of many popular myths has been the belief that what goes on in the mother's mind can have profound effects on the baby she is carrying: That marks or deformities could develop in a baby in resemblance to something which strongly impressed or frightened the mother during pregnancy; that by her listening to good music her child would be more musical; or by her reading elevating books the child would be brainier, etc. Actually there is no nerve connection between the mother and the baby, and no way her thoughts could reach the child—and certainly no way that her thinking could affect the child's genes. All that might happen is that her mental and nervous state, if good, might benefit her physical state, and therefore help the child; or, contrariwise, if she is badly upset during pregnancy, the nourishment and environment for the child might be worsened.

▶ *The mother's age.* While the genes the mother transmits to her baby are exactly the same whatever her age (since her eggs with their quotas of genes were formed before her own birth), the prenatal environment she provides may change as she grows older. For one thing, aging is apt to bring more diseases, internal upsets and disorders. Thus, with older mothers (mostly those beyond the late thirties), the risk of defects and abnormalities in babies may increase. (Example: *Mongolian idiocy,* in Chap. 17.) However, if the mother is healthy and fit in all ways, her age by itself may affect the child very little.

FATHER'S INFLUENCE ON CHILD. Once a father has made his contribution to the child's heredity at conception, by way of the sperm, his influence on the child's traits can be only those exerted after it is born. But as in the mother's case, the "like father, like son" theory often confuses environmental influences with hereditary effects. If a father's (or mother's) alcoholism, criminality, degeneracy or other bad traits are repeated in children, this need not at all mean that heredity is responsible. Nor can the repetition of good traits of behavior and temperament be necessarily credited to heredity. In every case the home environment and the hereditary histories of *both* parents must be weighed together.

▶ *The father's age.* Unlike the situation with the mother, the age of the father has nothing to do with the prenatal condition or development of a child. This follows from the fact that the *genes* in the father's sperms are in no way changed by his aging. So long as a man can go on producing fertile sperms (and some men have done so into their nineties), these sperms will be exactly the same in the quality and workings of their genes, and the traits they can produce in children, as the sperms of the man when he was young and robust. (The statement may be no surprise to livestock experts, who know that thoroughbred stallions and blooded bulls can be mated into their relatively old ages, without any deterioration in the quality of offspring.) Nor will the fact that a man has been seriously disabled in a war or an accident, or has acquired a serious disease, affect the *heredity* of his children.

3
The Workings of
Heredity

THE "MENDELIAN LAWS." These refer to the basic principles of heredity discovered by an Austrian monk, Gregor Mendel, in 1857. He was the abbot of a monastery at Brno (then in Austria, now in Czechoslovakia) where he had a garden in which he experimented. One series of Mendel's experiments, crossbreeding sweet peas of different varieties, brought to light the facts about inheritance which are now called the "Mendelian laws." These "laws," or principles, are:

1. Inherited traits are produced by separate factors (the "genes") which pass along unchanged from one generation to another.

2. The genes come in pairs in individuals, one of every pair from each parent, and if two paired genes differ in their effects, one usually dominates the other, and may be called "dominant," whereas the weaker gene, whose effects are suppressed, may be called "recessive."

3. When seeds are formed in plants (or sperms or eggs are formed in any animal or human), the two genes of each pair in the parent separate or segregate, and only one of each pair goes to an offspring. Which gene of a given pair goes into any seed, sperm or egg is independent of which gene of another pair goes into the same seed, sperm or egg. That is to say, if a plant has dominant genes producing red coloring and tallness, but also carries hidden recessive genes for white color and shortness, the "red" and "tall" genes might or might not go into the same seed. One seed could as easily get the "red" and "short" genes together, and another the "white" and "tall" genes.

▶ *Later findings.* The importance of Mendel's discoveries was not realized until after 1900, when various investigators checked

13

and found that the Mendelian laws apparently applied to inheritance in all living things, including human beings. However, in time it was shown that these "laws" needed certain qualifications and modifications. The most important strides in clarifying and extending the knowledge of heredity came through the researches of the late, great Professor Thomas Hunt Morgan and his brilliant Columbia University team, which included the now-famous Professor H. J. Muller (who, like Professor Morgan, was awarded a Nobel Prize). These scientists and others, experimenting mainly with fruit flies (*drosophila*), worked out many of the detailed principles and techniques which form the foundation of the science of modern genetics.

VARIETIES OF GENES. Each gene is a living molecule—a tiny bit of the living substance, *protoplasm.* (More precisely, the gene is a protein molecule, with its most vital constituent being "DNA"—*desoxyribonucleic acid.*) As chemists know, there are countless types and varieties of molecules, each with different properties, depending on the number, kind and arrangement of the atoms of which they are composed. So, too, there are countless types and varieties of gene-molecules, or genes. First, the genes of one species are different from those of other species. Cat genes are different from dog genes, cow genes from horse genes, ape genes from monkey genes. And human genes, of course, are different from the genes of all other animals—which is mainly why we are so different from them. Further, among human beings themselves, as within each species of other animals, there are different gradations and varieties of the genes for given traits. This in turn helps to explain (but is not the only reason) why one individual may be so different from another in a great many ways.

▶ *How genes work.* Each gene has a special chemical effect, or series of effects, on the materials which come into the individual, from conception onwards. In some respects a gene acts like an *enzyme* or *catalyst,* a substance which converts other substances into changed forms: As yeast causes dough to rise, or rennet turns milk into junket. When a baby is conceived, all of his genes begin to work on the raw materials in the fertilized

Varieties of Genes

Each gene in each chromosome has its special function.

Engineer

Architect

Carpenter

Mason

Plumber

Decorator

Chemist

In the paired chromosomes from the father and mother the genes at each place have the same assigned jobs.

-- But genes may do their jobs in different ways:

"BULLY" genes (dominant) may keep weaker ones (recessive) from working.

"FREAK" genes work peculiarly to produce various oddities in the body.

"TEMPERAMENTAL" genes (qualified) work unexpectedly and only under some circumstances.

"RIP VAN WINKLE" genes (late onset) may sleep for years and then awake to action.

"BUSY-BODY" genes (multi-action) do various jobs at once, and sometimes wreck many jobs.

"VILLAIN" genes produce serious defects and diseases, and sometimes cause early death.

egg, later on the food materials coming in from the mother. Through continuous stages the genes help to form many types of cells, produce flesh, bones and muscles, construct organs and get functions under way. In the first stages, when the general characteristics of the body are being shaped, all or a great many genes may work together on the same job. Later special genes begin to work on shapes of particular features, coloring and many other special details. If we likened genes to human workers, we could find among them every type of specialist, each with his own capacities: Laborers, architects, engineers, plumbers, chemists, decorators, sculptors, dieticians, doctors, etc. One need think only of the many thousands of details in the construction and functioning of the human body to realize how infinite a variety of "jobs" are engaged in and directed by the genes.

GENE MULTIPLICATION. One of the most important properties of the genes is their capacity for reproducing themselves. (It is mainly in this way that genes, as living molecules, differ from any mineral or non-living molecules.) The self-reproduction of the genes begins and proceeds with fantastic rapidity from the moment a new baby is conceived. As we saw in Chapter 2, the father's sperm brings into the egg twenty-four separate chromosomes—each a string of genes. Waiting in the mother's egg are another twenty-four chromosomes. Immediately the chromosomes and their genes begin to "fatten up" on the material in the egg, and each gene doubles in size (or builds a replica alongside itself). Then, as each fattened chromosome splits in two lengthwise, each doubled gene at the same time also divides. Finally the cell housing the chromosomes pinches together, and the two halves separate, so that there now are two cells, each with exact duplicates of all the original forty-eight chromosomes and their genes. (*See illustration.*) The process is repeated again and again, the two cells becoming four, the four eight, the eight sixteen, etc., into the millions, billions and trillions. (It is estimated that a baby at birth has about twenty-six trillion cells, with the same genes in each cell. The total number of these genes is still unknown. Present estimates range very roughly from a minimum of about 40,000 to 60,000 or more genes in the 24 pairs of human chromosomes that go into every human cell.)

CELL AND GENE SPECIALIZATION. While the chromosomes and genes that go into every cell are exactly the same, the cells as they form and develop are *not* the same. This is because with each step in the cell-multiplication process, somewhat as with material in a house being built, cells at different points are shaped and constructed in different ways. Under the direction of the "specialist" genes we mentioned previously, cell clusters

How Chromosomes Multiply

1.   2.   3.   4.

(1) One of the original 48 chromosomes in a fertilized egg cell.

(2) Each gene in the chromosome creates a replica of itself.

(3) When the genes are duplicated, the doubled chromosome splits.

—This has been occurring likewise in all the other 47 chromosomes in the egg cell.

(4) The duplicated chromosomes move apart and the cell divides, forming two cells, each housing exact duplicates of all the original 48 chromosomes.

take different forms. Some turn into the outer parts of the body —skin, muscles, features; some into the skeletal framework; some into the internal mechanisms—brain and nervous system, heart and arteries, digestive system, glands, etc. Precisely how this is done (or how experts believe it is done) is far too complicated to explain here. But there is no guess about *what* is done. Innumerable studies of embryos show to what point the body construction has been carried out at every successive stage. And the fact that at any given stage—four weeks, eight weeks, twelve weeks, etc.—the development of any normal baby is almost identical with that of any other is proof of how remarkably systematic and precise the human "specialist" genes are in their workings.

▶ *"Gene-specialist" differences.* Apart from completing given stages of the baby's development at prescribed times, the "specialist" genes are highly individual in their work, just as are human architects, carpenters, decorators, engineers, etc. One "eye-color" gene may make eyes dark, another may be set on making them light blue, another green, etc. For hair color there are "black," "brown," "blond" and "red" genes. Innumerable other differences in genes account largely for the varieties of human features and body details, and to a greater or lesser extent for differences in physical and mental functioning, and in fitness or defectiveness (always allowing for environmental influences).

WHY CHILDREN OF A FAMILY DIFFER. The fact that there are many differences among genes for given traits does not of itself explain why two children of the same parents are often so very different in their heredity. For if every child in a family received *all* of the father's genes, and *all* of the mother's genes, then one child's hereditary makeup would be exactly the same as another's. This does not happen (except with identical twins) because, as noted under the "Mendelian Laws," each sperm of the father carries only *half* of his chromosomes, and each egg of the mother carries only *half* of hers. In other words, when a man produces sperms there is a process whereby for every two sperms, his twenty-four pairs of chromosomes sort out into two groups, with *only one chromosome of each pair* going in each group, around which a sperm then takes shape. Thus, every sperm contains twenty-four *single* chromosomes. When eggs are formed in the female there is a similar process whereby each egg gets only one of each pair of her chromosomes, so that it also carries only twenty-four single chromosomes.

▶ *Sorting out of chromosomes.* In either parent's case, which chromosomes of any pair go into which sperms is entirely a matter of chance. The process is much like a shuffling and dealing out of cards, but with chromosomes being dealt out instead. One sperm might get a combination of chromosomes quite dif-

How Heredity Works

**Father's
chromosomes**

Each parent has
24 pairs of
chromosomes,
or 48 in all.

**Mother's
chromosomes**

When father produces sperms,
each sperm gets only half of his
chromosomes.

When mother produces eggs,
each egg gets only half of her
chromosomes.

As the sperm fertilizes the egg,
the 24 chromosomes from the
father join with the 24 chromosomes from the mother.

The combined
48 chromosomes
work to produce
all of the baby's
hereditary traits.

ferent or even entirely different from those in another sperm; or again, most of the chromosomes in two sperms might be the same. This is equally true for the chromosomes in the mother's eggs. But the chances that any two children in a family (other than identical twins) would get exactly the same chromosome combinations—or completely different chromosomes—is extremely remote, for reasons which follow.

▶ *Possible chromosome combinations.* Taking at random one out of each of the twenty-four pairs of chromosomes carried by every man—this chromosome out of one pair, that chromosome out of another pair—it would be possible for him to produce sperms with 16,777,216 different chromosome combinations. A woman's eggs, likewise, could carry any of 16,777,216 different chromosome combinations. Together, then, the sperms and eggs of any couple could produce any of about three hundred million million (300,000,000,000,000) different chromosome combinations—which would be, theoretically, the possible hereditary varieties of the children they could have. Ordinarily, however, about half the chromosomes—or a few more or a few less—of any two children of a family would be the same. Nor would the *unlike* chromosomes necessarily be different in all their genes. In fact, if the grandparents on either side (and especially on both sides) were of similar stocks and alike in many traits, the different chromosomes would be carrying many matching genes. In sum, the hereditary likenesses or differences among children in a family will depend on how many genes they have in common, and what differences there are in their other genes.

▶ *"Dominance" and "recessiveness."* How a difference in only a few genes can often produce a marked difference between two children of a family becomes clear if we recall the Mendelian principle regarding "dominant" and "recessive" genes. Suppose a parent carries a gene of each type for a given trait, and that one child receives the dominant, the other the recessive: As for eye color, if one child receives a "black-eye" gene, the other only a "blue-eye" gene; or for hair form, if one child receives a "curly" gene, the other only a "straight" gene. In these cases, one child will show the dominant trait, and if another child gets a recessive gene from each parent, he will show the recessive trait. The differences with respect to most traits may be unimportant. But there are some genetic situations where a single dominant gene (or its absence) in one child, and not in another, can produce striking differences in their appearance, mentality, talent, health, or strength and in the whole course of their lives. Examples of these genetic situations, and of various others, will be found in succeeding chapters.

GENE CHANGES (MUTATIONS). We have previously stated that the genes a parent passes on to a child are unaltered by any changes the parent has made (or that have been made) in his own traits during his or her lifetime. But we also noted that in extremely rare instances a gene *can be changed* in its workings (though not in accordance with any change in the parent's traits). The gene change or *mutation* to which we refer may take place if a gene in one of the germ cells of a prospective father or a mother is "hit" or disturbed by some outside force in such a way as to shake up, rearrange or alter the atoms composing it. Under natural conditions, cosmic rays, chemicals and perhaps other outside influences can produce mutations, as they have been doing from the beginning of life on earth. (See Chap. 25.) These natural gene changes, accumulating through the ages, have been responsible for producing the infinite varieties of genes among human beings and all other living things; and in our own time spontaneous mutations, as they have been capitalized on, have made possible the breeding of many new types of domestic animals, plants and flowers. However, it should be stressed that in the great majority of cases mutations are very slight; that in only about one in one hundred instances are they beneficial or useful; and that for the rest, they tend mostly to produce defects in the genes which, under natural conditions, would eventually cause such genes to be weeded out.

▶ *Artificially induced mutations.* The possibilities that have begun to loom up with respect to the mutation-inducing effects of radiation—particularly through atomic and hydrogen bombs—will be discussed in Chapter 27.

REASONS FOR OPTIMISM. Altogether, as the reader will find, the facts about human heredity uncovered by scientists are mostly on the optimistic side. Many conditions formerly regarded

as due to bad or defective inheritance have been traced to bad
environments; and as environments have improved, the incidence
of these conditions and their threats have been greatly reduced.
Even where conditions are known to be hereditary, recent findings have in many instances helped to lessen the fears regarding
them. Not least among the helpful developments has been the
disproof of old theories about the inheritance of acquired characteristics (Chaps. 2, 25). Parents now know that any mistakes
they made, any diseases, defects or bad habits they acquired,
or any shortcomings developed by unfavorable environments,
did not "soak into" their genes, and cannot be transmitted to
their children. At the same time, what parents have learned to
advantage can be transmitted to their children through improved
environment and proper training. The forces of heredity still
remain and always will be vastly powerful. But more can be
done now to give good heredity—with which the great majority
of people are endowed—a chance to assert itself, and to keep
bad heredity—which is found in only a very small proportion of
people—from doing its worst.

4

The Baby's Sex

"WE WANT A BOY"; "WE WANT A GIRL." Isn't there something parents can do beforehand to make their wish as to the baby's sex come true? Not yet! Throughout the ages parents have had the same thought, and countless "sex-determining" formulas and treatments have been employed. All those in the past were worthless because they were based on false notions and superstitions about the way in which a baby's sex is determined. But even today, although we *do* know what causes a baby to be a boy or a girl—as we shall presently see—there is still no way of insuring the desired results. The sex of the baby continues to be a matter of chance—although it need not always remain so.

▶ *How sex is determined.* The sex of every baby is fixed at the moment of conception. The deciding factor comes not through the mother, but through the *father's contribution.* Whether the baby will be a boy or a girl depends simply on which *of two types of sperms from the father enters the egg first.* One kind of sperm leads to the production of a boy. The other kind of sperm results in a girl. The mother's egg is neutral: When it is fertilized it can work to produce either a boy or a girl, depending on which kind of sperm enters the egg and starts the development of the baby.

THE "SEX" CHROMOSOMES. Hereditary factors—chromosomes and their genes—determine the baby's sex, as they do other inherited traits. In Chapter 2 we saw that at conception every child receives forty-eight chromosomes—a set of twenty-four from the father, a set of twenty-four from the mother. In each of these two sets, one special chromosome is called the "sex" chromosome because it is concerned with the determina-

23

tion of the baby's sex. These sex chromosomes are of two types. One type is very long, containing many genes, and is called the "X" chromosome. The other is very short, with few genes, and is called the "Y" chromosome. And the whole difference to start with between what will be a girl, and what will be a boy, is that the girl gets *two* X chromosomes, or an "XX" combination; the boy gets only *one* X, *plus one* Y—an "XY" combination.

▶ *How are the "sex" chromosomes transmitted?* When a woman produces eggs, there is a process whereby each egg receives replicas of only *half* of her chromosomes—or *one* chromosome of each of her twenty-four pairs. Since her sex chromosomes are *both* Xs, one X will go into every egg. Thus, the mother transmits an X chromosome to *every* child. But the father's contribution works differently. When he produces sperms, there also is a process whereby each sperm receives only *one* of every pair of his chromosomes. So, since his sex chromosomes are of two kinds, X and Y, his sperms will also be of two kinds. Of every two sperms the man produces, an X chromosome will go into one, a Y into the other. Which means that of the tens of millions of sperms which a father releases at a given time, exactly half are X-bearers, half Y-bearers.

▶ *The "X" and "Y" race.* As the millions of sperms enter the womb and move up into the tube where the egg is waiting, one may think of it as a race between the Ys and the Xs to get to the egg first and win it for the male side or the female side. Since the egg already carries one X, as we have seen, the baby's sex will depend on whether the entering sperm carries another X, or carries a Y. (Only a single sperm decides [Chap. 2], because the moment one sperm enters, all the others are shut out.) Thus, if an X sperm wins out, it will join with the X already there and an XX individual—a girl baby—will be started on her way. But if a Y wins, the result will be an XY individual—a boy. All this is shown in our accompanying diagram. Study it and fix it in your mind. The facts will come up many times in this book, and in your life.

THE "SEX-GENE" BALANCE. How does the XX combination cause the baby to develop as a girl, the XY combination to develop as a boy? The answer lies in the fact that while "sex" genes are found in various chromosomes, the X is heavily loaded with "femaleness" genes, whereas the other chromosomes together carry more "maleness" genes. These "maleness" genes can outweigh the "femaleness" genes in a single X, but not in *two* Xs. So if an X-bearing sperm enters the egg, joining with the X already there, the combined "femaleness" genes in the two Xs throw the development of the baby toward femaleness. But when a little Y chromosome enters the egg, bringing no additional "femaleness" genes, the "maleness" genes in the other chromosomes can predominate, and cause the baby to develop

How a Baby's Sex Is Determined

MOTHER'S EGGS all carry a large sex chromosome—the "X"

FATHER'S SPERMS are of two kinds:

other 23 chromosomes

. . . one of every two carries an "X"

. . . one of every two carries a small "Y"

IF a sperm with an "X" enters an egg—

"XX" combination

Result: A GIRL

IF a sperm with a "Y" enters an egg—

"XY" combination

Result: A BOY

as a boy. The Y chromosome is actually a blank so far as sex determination is concerned, and can be said to "merely go along for the ride." Among its few genes there are probably no "sex" genes. It is therefore not the presence of the Y but the absence of an additional X that produces a male. In fact, there are species of animals which have no Y at all, the males being produced simply by one X, the females by two Xs.

Sex-Changing. Can a baby's sex be changed during the period before birth? No, once the baby has begun to develop as a boy, it cannot be turned into a girl, nor can a developing girl fetus be turned into a boy. (Even more impossible are the claims that mature men have been or could be transformed into women by "operations" or treatments. See "Sex Abnormalities," Chap. 13.) However, once in a thousand times, something may happen in prenatal life to throw sexual development from its proper course, and a boy may result whose sex organs are so incompletely developed that he may be mistaken for a girl; or a girl with abnormal development of her sex organs may be mistaken for a boy. Only in extremely rare instances is there a completely "in-between" individual who is neither properly male nor female. (For further details about this, and also about tests for establishing "sex identity," see again "Sex Abnormalities," Chap. 13.)

WHY MORE BOYS? A remarkable fact is that year after year, among the many millions of babies born in the United States and most other countries, there is an excess of boys by almost exactly the same percentage: For every 100 girls born, there will be close to 106 boys. This is definitely not because boys are "stronger" and achieve birth more easily. The contrary is true, as we shall see. It is because many more boys than girls are conceived. How can this be if the male-producing sperms (the Y-bearers) and the female-producing sperms (the X-bearers) are sent out in exactly equal numbers? Apparently the Y-bearing sperms have some advantages over the X-sperms in speed or chemical reactions, which enable them to win the race to the egg oftener, or to more readily fertilize the egg.

▶ *Male fetuses weaker.* One reason why Nature may cause more boys to be conceived is that they have less chance of surviving than have females. Contrary to the long-standing belief that males are hardier than females, science has now established that males actually are much likelier to be defective, and less able to withstand bad conditions than are females. This applies to every stage of life, but is most significant in the prenatal stages, when the environment for males and females is the same. Among the babies miscarried in the first few months the males outnumber the females by two or three to one; and among those dying shortly before or immediately after birth there are about 130 boys to 100 girls. Moreover, the risk of being abnormal or defective is much greater for boy babies. When added to this is the fact that in almost every stage of life thereafter the male death rate is markedly higher, there is a very good reason why more males should be needed at the start.

VARIATIONS IN THE SEX RATIO. Although the ratio among all babies born each year averages out close to 106 boys to 100 girls, the chances of having a boy may be above or below this average for mothers of different groups, ages and physical conditions. Because boy fetuses are weaker, the general rule seems to be that where prenatal conditions are best, there is a greater chance for boy babies to achieve birth. Thus, among the more favored groups there may possibly be up to 115 boys born for every 100 girls; in underprivileged groups, the ratio of boy to girl babies may be 103 or less. Moreover, in each group the healthiest young mothers, aged eighteen to twenty-two, have the greatest chance of producing boys—especially when it is the *first* birth—while among mothers aged thirty-eight to forty-two and over, the chances of having a boy may be less than even.

▶ *Twins, triplets.* Since male fetuses suffer more under unfavorable pre-birth conditions, it is not surprising that the more crowded the womb, the less are the relative chances that males will survive. In twin births the ratio drops to 103.5 boys to 100 girls; in triplets, 98 boys to 100 girls; in quadruplets, 70 boys to 100 girls.

▶ *Wartime births: More boys?* There is a long-standing belief that the ratio of boys born goes up during and immediately after wars, perhaps because Nature is trying to help make up for the men killed off. The evidence for World Wars I and II supports this only slightly. After World War I an increase of from 1 to

2.5 per cent in the boy ratio was reported in some countries of Europe, but not in the United States. During World War II and its aftermath much smaller increases were reported. To the extent that any increases in the boy ratio occur, scientists ascribe it not to mysterious influences, but to the fact that in the war periods there are relatively more first births, and more babies born to the younger, healthier mothers whose chance of having boys is above average.

HEREDITARY INFLUENCES IN SEX DETERMINATION. Where parents have three or four children all of the same sex, this may easily be as much a matter of chance as tossing coins and having them turn up three or four heads in a row. But where one finds families with up to twelve sons and no daughters (or vice versa), and families heavily slanted for several generations toward children of one sex, the possibility arises that hereditary influences may be at work. The only real evidence in this direction comes from experiments with lower animals, in which strains have been bred with tendencies to produce much higher than average ratios of either males or females, as desired. While no such breeding has taken place among humans, it is not unlikely that in some families or individuals there also are inborn tendencies which would favor the production of offspring of one sex rather than the other. These tendencies might work directly through stronger "sex" genes of either type carried in the sperms or eggs, or indirectly through special factors in the environment of the mother's womb. But all of this still is theoretical so far as human beings are concerned. (*Note:* A record all-son family in the United States at this writing is that of the Emory Harrison couple of Johnson City, Tennessee, with thirteen sons living, one son dead, and no daughters.)

"Sex-Determining" Methods. In recent years much publicity has been given one "scientific method" or another for helping parents to have a baby of the sex they desire. As stated at the outset, none of these methods has proved to be effective. This applies, for example, to the "acid-alkali" treatment ("acid" for a girl, "alkali" for a boy). Also unproved is the theory that a boy is more likely to result if the mother conceives in the latter part of her fertile period. But scientists do believe that eventually means may be found of influencing the chances of having either a boy or a girl, as desired. Possible methods may include: 1) Separating the father's Y-bearing from the X-bearing sperms in a laboratory, and inseminating the mother with the desired type; or 2) injecting chemical preparations in the mother which will have different effects on the boy-producing or girl-producing sperms.

▶ *Forecasting the expected baby's sex.* It may be distinctly possible soon—if not already possible by the time you read this book—for parents to know the sex of an expected baby months before its birth. Differences in the types of hormones produced by a boy fetus, as compared with a girl fetus, or in other chemical reactions, may show up in tests of the mother. Also, recently reported by Israeli scientists and others, a sample of cells of the fetus itself, if obtainable from the amniotic fluid, can reveal the expected baby's sex. (See also *"Sex identity tests,"* page 106.)

Your Own Chances of Having Boys or Girls. Throughout this chapter we have been speaking in terms of general averages as applied to millions of births each year. In your own case, with very few children involved, or with your mind on a single baby, the results may easily be different from the general odds. While it remains true that young, healthy mothers tend to produce more sons than do equal numbers of older, less healthy mothers, the reader (or the reader's wife) may be a young, healthy woman and yet have three or four girls and no boy; and a much older, sickly mother next door may have nothing but boys. Nor will the fact that you have had three girls, or three boys in a row, increase the chance that the next will be of the opposite sex. However, it is worth noting that the emphasis on having a child of one specific sex is becoming less marked in most advanced countries, particularly in the United States, where a growing number of parents see equal advantages in having girls or boys.

THE SEX GENES AFTER BIRTH. Do the sex genes stop working at birth? No, they continue to influence the sexual development of the body and its functioning throughout life. In the normal male the predominant "maleness" genes and the processes they set in motion will direct the production at the prescribed stages of all the many special masculine physical traits and functions—male sex organs, sex glands and sperm production, bigger and heavier bones and muscles, beard, etc. In the female the stronger balance of "femaleness" genes will direct the development of all her many special physical characteristics and functions—her sex organs and glands, egg production, menstruation, preparation for childbearing and nursing, and the various distinguishing characteristics of her body as compared with that of the male. (In later chapters we shall also see how the sex genes affect the types and incidences of diseases and defects in males and females.) Although environmental factors are also constantly at work, the sex genes largely dictate when puberty begins, when sexual development reaches its fullest point, when childbearing capacities in women cease, etc., as well as influencing many aspects of the behavior in the two sexes. (Additional discussions on these points, Chap. 24.)

5
Twins, "Trips,"
"Quads," "Quints"

TWIN TYPES. The first thing to know about twins is whether they are "identicals" or "fraternals." Confusion may create many difficulties in rearing twins, in their adjustment to each other, and in medical diagnosis of their ailments.

▶ *Identical twins.* These are the "one-egg" twins, who are products of the same single egg and the same single sperm. Identical twins result when what started out to be a single baby becomes *two* babies by a splitting of the fertilized egg at a very early stage. In the process each twin gets duplicates of exactly the same chromosomes and genes, so that both have *identical heredity.* For this reason, also, identical twins *must always be of the same sex,* either two boys or two girls. But even though identical twins have exactly the same genes (and with respect to their hereditary factors are actually the same person in duplicate), their environments in the womb and after they are born may be different enough to keep them from ever being exactly the same in appearance, health and behavior. Sometimes these differences are quite marked. Usually, however, it is hard to tell identical twins apart, and frequently their remarkable similarities continue until the end of their lives.

▶ *Fraternal twins.* These are the "two-egg" twins, products of two different eggs and two different sperms. They make up the majority of the twins—about 70 per cent. (That is, of all twins born, more than two out of three pairs are fraternals.) Even though fraternal twins are carried in the womb and born together, they need be no more alike than any two children of a family who are born separately. In about half the cases fraternal twins are different in sex; one in four times both are boys, one in four times both are girls. Fraternal twins just happen to

31

be conceived at about the same time, when a mother produces two eggs instead of the usual one, and each egg is fertilized by a different sperm. (In rare instances one of a pair of fraternal twins may be conceived several days, or even a week or more, after the other.)

DIAGNOSING TWINS. Telling whether twins are identical or fraternal is not always easy, and mistakes are often made (although not nearly as much so as in the past). At birth one cannot go by the old theory that if like-sexed twins have the same placenta and fetal sac, this proves they are identical, whereas the presence of different placentas and sacs proves they are fraternal. It is now known that in some instances identical twins may develop separate placentas and sacs; conversely, in fraternal twins the sacs and placentas may sometimes be fused and appear to be one. Again, while generally true that twins who look remarkably alike are identicals, there are exceptions. Sometimes an early mishap or some unusual condition in the womb discriminating against one of an identical pair may cause him or her to look and be quite different from the other in various respects. On the other hand, just as two non-twin brothers or sisters may look remarkably alike, some fraternal twins also may look so much alike as to be mistaken for identicals.

▶ *Twin tests.* To resolve doubts, a number of tests can now be made which will prove quite clearly if twins are fraternal or identical. The first test is for the blood types—A, B, O; Rh; M, N, etc. (explained in Chapter 15). If the twins have blood-type differences, this is immediate proof that they are *not* identicals. But should their blood types be the same, this still does not mean that they might not be a fraternal pair. Further clarifying tests may be for their similarities or dissimilarities in eye color, eyesight, skin and hair color, hair form; finger-, palm- and footprints; blood pressure, pulse, respiration, brain-wave patterns; and various hereditary peculiarities or abnormalities. (In cases where the problem of twin diagnosis is complex, consult one of the heredity clinics or some medical geneticist. See Appendix.)

▶ *Twin transplants.* An unusual and special characteristic of identical twins is that any tissue or organ from one can be successfully transplanted and take root in the body of the other.

How Twins Are Produced

IDENTICAL TWINS

—result from the same single egg and single sperm.

After the egg begins to grow it divides into equal halves with duplicated chromosomes.

The halves go on to become two babies, with exactly the same hereditary factors.

IDENTICAL twins are always the same sex (either two boys or two girls). They usually look much alike. They have exactly the same eye color, hair color, hair form, blood types and all other hereditary traits.

FRATERNAL TWINS

—result from two different eggs, fertilized by two different sperms.

The two different fertilized eggs develop separately into two different embryos.

The two embryos grow into two babies with different hereditary factors.

FRATERNAL twins may be either of the same sex (two boys or two girls), or different in sex (a boy and a girl). They may be different in looks, coloring, hair form, blood types, and other hereditary traits.

In the case of non-identical twins, as of any two genetically different persons, a transplant will "take" only temporarily. An operation reported in 1955 was that of an entire kidney taken from one identical twin and successfully transplanted in his brother.

"MIRROR-IMAGING" AND LEFT-HANDEDNESS. "Mirror-imaging" refers to the peculiarity found in about one in four pairs of identical twins, in which a birthmark, or some oddity in a tooth, feature, or organ of the body, appears on the right side of one twin and the left side of another. Such reverse patterning results from the fact that when the halves of the same embryo separate to form the identical twins, certain characteristics may appear on opposite sides, somewhat as with the cut halves of an apple or a melon.

▶ *Left-handedness.* Often, but not always related to mirror-imaging in identical twins is the unusually large number among them who are left-handed, when the other twin of the pair is right-handed. This occurs in about 20 per cent of the identical twins. That "mirror-imaging" is not the only factor is shown by this evidence: 1) In about 2 per cent of identical twin pairs, *both* are left-handed; 2) among fraternal twins there also is an above-average incidence of left-handedness; and 3) in non-twins left-handedness may be produced by an hereditary tendency, which is influenced by environmental factors. One added reason for the high incidence in twins may be the crowded prenatal conditions which may make it more likely for left-handedness to develop in one twin, particularly if the hereditary "susceptibility" is present.

▶ *Heredity and left-handedness.* Among non-twins, Dr. D. C. Rife has reported that if both parents are left-handed, there is a fifty-fifty chance a child will be a "leftie"; where just one parent is left-handed, there is a 16 per cent chance; where both parents are right-handed, there is only about a 6 per cent chance a given child will be a "leftie."

"Siamese" Twins. These and other freak twins may result when the division of an egg or an embryo in forming two identical twins is not complete. The twins may then be born joined at their breasts, hips, shoulders or heads. (The famed circus pair from Siam from whom the name derives were joined at the hip.) It is estimated that Siamese twins occur about once in 50,000 births. Few of these twins survive into maturity. In the past, operations to separate Siamese twins usually failed, but in recent years improved operative techniques have led to a number of successful separations. The worst freaks are those in whom the early embryonic separation is only partial, resulting in monsters with two heads and one body, or one body and four arms and four legs, etc. Most of these, fortunately, die before birth.

CHANCES OF HAVING TWINS. The incidence of twinning varies in different countries and among mothers of different races and groups. The proportions of identical as compared with fraternal twins also vary. In the United States twins occur on the average about once in from 85 to 90 births among White mothers, and about once in 76 births among Negro mothers. Higher twin ratios are reported in some countries, lower ratios in others. Some recent figures: Denmark, 1 twin pair in 62; Finland, 1 in 68; Sweden, 1 in 69; Italy, 1 in 77; Germany, 1 in 82; France and Australia, 1 in 92; Spain, 1 in 111. Twins are least frequent among Mongolians (Japanese, Chinese and American Indians), with reports of fewer than one twin pair in 170 births. Another unusual situation is that while among Whites the estimated ratio is from two to three fraternal pairs to one identical twin pair, in Japan identicals are said to be almost as frequent as fraternals.

▶ *Inherited twinning tendencies.* There are strong indications that heredity plays an important part in twinning. Repeated sets of twins occur in many families apparently much beyond random chance, as in the John Burg family of Wisconsin, with five pairs of twins among seventeen children. Also in some lower animals which ordinarily have single offspring (cattle, sheep, goats), breeds especially prone to twinning are known. Among humans, about one in five women is believed to have a marked twinning tendency. The causes of twinning are complex and still in doubt. But where heredity may play a part, there appear to be different genes for the two types of twinning: For producing identical twins, the genes may be ones which stimulate an egg to split at an early stage. For fraternal twins, the genes may stimulate the mother's ovaries to produce two eggs at a time, instead of one. (In very rare instances a woman may have two separate wombs, in each of which she can carry a child.)

▶ *Mother's age and twinning.* In all groups, older mothers on the average have a much greater chance of bearing twins than have very young mothers. For American mothers the greatest chance of having twins comes to those who are pregnant in their late 30s, with about one twin pair in 60 births; least for those in their teens, with only one twin pair in about 165 births. The difference stems mainly from the much higher proportion of *fraternal* twins born to older mothers, presumably because they are much more likely than younger mothers to produce two eggs at a time. The mother's age has much less effect on the production of identical twins.

▶ *"Lost" twins.* Undoubtedly many more twins are conceived (perhaps several times as many) as the number achieving birth. In innumerable cases one of the twins may die off at a very early stage and be absorbed in the mother's body. In rare instances a tiny embryonic twin is found inside the body of the surviving twin, encased in a tumor.

TRIPS, QUADS AND QUINTS. Most of the general facts regarding two-at-a-time babies apply to the higher multiples. The distinctions between "identicals" and "fraternals" also hold for triplets, quadruplets or quintuplets, with the difference that since more than two are involved, one may find among these multiple sets combinations of both identicals and fraternals, as well as all of one type or the other. (Examples later.)

▶ *Incidences of trips, quads, etc.* For large populations or the world as a whole, there seems to be a remarkable natural formula at work governing the relative incidences of twins, triplets, quadruplets and quintuplets. Known as "Hellin's law" (after its German discoverer, D. Hellin), this formula provides that the incidence of triplets will be the square of the ratio of twins to single births; of quadruplets, the cube of the incidence of twins; of quintuplets, the fourth power of the incidence of twins. Thus, if twins occur once in 90 births, triplets should occur once in 90 times 90, or 8,100 births; quadruplets, once in 90 times 90 times 90, or 729,000 births; quintuplets, once in the latter number by 90 again, or 65,610,000 births. The ratios in the United States in recent years for triplets and quadruplets have come closely to the formula. (Quintuplets are too rare for us to know how well the formula might apply.)

TRIPLETS. As with twins, a set of three babies born together may all be "identicals"—the products of a single egg and a single sperm; or they may all be "fraternals"—the products of different eggs and different sperms. But there is another possibility: Two of the triplets may be identical twins who came from one fertilized egg, and the third triplet may have come from a different egg, and thus be a "fraternal" twin in relation to the other two. Here is how the three different types of triplet sets are produced:

▶ *One-egg triplets* (all identicals). These result when a *single* fertilized egg first splits in half to form twin embryos. One half remains set, developing into one baby; the other half splits again, to produce two more babies. All three of these triplets carry exactly the same genes, are always of the same sex, and are as much alike one another as are identical twins.

▶ *Two-egg triplets.* These start off at conception as a pair of fraternal twins arising from *two different* fertilized eggs. One of these twin embryos then splits in half to become two individuals, who are identical twins. The other triplet, from the second egg, is a fraternal twin in relation to the two identicals. Two-egg triplets can be all of the same sex, three boys or three girls; or a mixed set—two boys and a girl, or two girls and a boy.

▶ *Three-egg triplets.* These (probably the least common) result when a mother produces three eggs at the same time, and each egg is fertilized by a different sperm. Such unmatched triplets are all fraternal in relation to one another, each being different in hereditary factors, with no more biological likenesses in common than have any three children of a family born at different times. As with two-egg triplets, they can all be of the same sex, or two of one sex, the third of the opposite sex.

QUADRUPLETS. When four babies are born together, they may have the following relationships:

▶ *One-egg quads.* Products of a single fertilized egg which divided in two, each half re-dividing again to form four embryos with identical heredity, and always of the same sex.

▶ *Two-egg quads.* Products of two separate fertilized eggs. May be either two pairs of identical twins, one pair from each egg; or a set of identical triplets, from one egg, with the fourth member from the other egg.

▶ *Three-egg quads.* Products of three separate fertilized eggs, two of which remain set, to produce two babies, while the third splits to form two more. The last two are identicals, the other two fraternals in relation to them and to each other.

▶ *Four-egg quads.* Each from a different fertilized egg, and all fraternals in relation to one another.

QUINTUPLETS. These may be theoretically of five main types, products of one egg or of two, three, four or five eggs, and in various combinations of identicals and fraternals. The world-famous Dionne quintuplets, born in Canada in 1934 (the first recorded quintuplet set in which all five survived and who remained as a unit until Emilie's death in 1954), were proved to be an *all-identical* set, derived from the same single fertilized egg. Experts believe that this egg began by splitting in two, then each of the halves splitting again to form four embryos. Three of these four embryos remained set, to become Yvonne, Annette and Cecile. The fourth embryo split again, to form Emilie and Marie. The special relationship between these last two was indicated by the "mirror-imaging" which they showed in several details (hair-whorls, handedness, etc.); and the probability that they were last to develop was strengthened by the fact that they were the weakest of the five. (Marie was the frailest, and still is, but Emilie had an epileptic condition which indirectly led to her death through suffocation while asleep. There is no evidence of epileptic symptoms in any of the other five, which suggests that Emilie's condition was due to some environmental mishap, possibly even in prenatal life.)

▶ *The Diligentis.* These five, born in Argentina in 1943, are the only living quintuplets at this writing. They are three boys and two girls, but their relationship has not been clearly established. There is some indication, however, that they are either a three-egg or a four-egg set.

WHY WE STUDY TWINS. If you have a set of twins (or trips or quads!), particularly identicals, you will soon find that geneticists, doctors and psychologists are much interested in them. The study of twins offers us some of our most important clues as to the degree in which human traits are hereditary or environmental. For instance, since identical twins carry exactly the same genes, any differences between them must be due to environment. This applies to differences in stature, body-build, features or health, as well as to differences in IQ, behavior, achievement and personality. The greater the difference in any trait between identical twins, the more strongly it points to the role of environment in helping to produce that trait. (As noted before, different environmental influences may be exerted on identical twins from the time they begin to develop in the womb.) On the other hand, where identical twins are raised in very different environments, as in cases of those separated in infancy and reared by different foster parents, remarkable similarities may yet appear in their physical makeup, diseases and defects, and often in mental qualities and capacities. These similarities offer evidence of the role of heredity. Finally, when identical twins are compared with fraternal twins, the relative degrees of similarity or difference between paired twins of the two types may offer important clues as to the comparative influences of heredity and environment. (Twin studies will be dealt with again at various later points in this book. See Index for specific references.)

6
Predicting
Children's Looks

WHY PARENTS ARE INTERESTED. People wonder what their children will look like for more reasons than mere curiosity. *Pride:* Individuals are flattered when their children resemble them (at least in the desirable aspects), and relatives may be partial to the child who is most like them or their side of the family. *Jealousy:* Suspicious husbands are reassured if their children have some of their distinctive traits. *Good looks:* Of most concern is that the child—particularly if a girl—be good-looking. On the latter point, fortunately, the chances that a daughter will be pretty or a son handsome are much greater today than ever before in most countries. The genes for looks have not changed, but environments have. Great improvements in diet, health, living conditions and medical and dental care are steadily helping to produce better-looking, better-built and taller young people, and very few grow up to be really "homely."

FORECASTING A CHILD'S LOOKS. If human beings were bred as are cats, dogs or blooded livestock, predictions regarding the looks of an expected child would be easy. Through many successive generations of controlled breeding of domesticated animals, the genes of particular breeds have been so selected and fixed that there is little doubt about the size, shape, coloring and feature details of offspring of a given mating. But human beings have at no time been bred so deliberately. Every person today is a descendant of a great many ancestors of varied types, and carries a haphazard collection of hundreds of genes governing body structure and outward appearance. Many of these genes—the "dominant" ones—reveal themselves by the surface traits they produce. But many other genes—the "recessives"—may have their effects suppressed in the parents, though they can assert themselves in a child. It is in the latter way that various unexpected and sometimes baffling traits may appear in children.

▶ *Specific feature forecasts.* Any forecast of what the expected children of a given couple will look like is largely a matter of knowing or guessing what genes for the traits in question the parents carry, and then estimating the chances that their children will inherit the gene-combinations required to produce these traits. If the parents are fairly similar in coloring and important features, and are of the same ethnic and/or racial stocks, they are likely to be carrying many matching genes for the traits they themselves show. Their children, then, are apt to inherit gene-combinations which will make them resemble not only their parents, but their brothers and sisters, in many details. But when the parents are very different in coloring and features, and are of different stocks, their children can inherit any of numerous gene-combinations. In such cases it is possible for a child to look not only unlike the parents, but unlike other children in the family. However, conclusions about this cannot be drawn until maturity, because family resemblances often come out and increase with age.

ODDS IN FEATURE INHERITANCE. With respect to many traits that given couples show, geneticists can say there is an almost 100 per cent chance that these will reappear in their children. But there are many other traits where the expectancy of appearance in children can be stated only in terms of odds, such as a "one-in-two chance," or a "one-in-four chance," or even more reduced chances. All of such fractional forecasts are based on the knowledge of how the genes for a given trait work according to the principles of *dominance* and *recessiveness*, explained in Chapter 3 (The "Mendelian Laws"). Here are some of the possibilities of transmission:

1. If *either* parent has a dominant trait (such as dark eyes) and the other parent has the corresponding recessive trait (such as blue eyes), there is at best a fifty-fifty chance any child will show the recessive trait. This will depend on whether the parent with the dominant trait is also carrying a hidden recessive gene for the trait. But if this parent is not carrying the recessive gene, every child will show the dominant trait.

2. If both parents have a given dominant trait (such as dark eyes or dark hair), there is at best only a one-in-four chance a child will show the corresponding recessive trait (such as light-colored eyes, or blond hair). This can happen only if each parent is carrying a hidden recessive gene for the trait, paired with the dominant gene, and the two recessive genes come together in a child. Obviously, if both parents carry only dominant genes for a trait, there is no chance a child will show the recessive trait.

3. If both parents show a recessive trait (blue eyes, or blond hair, etc.), which means neither is carrying the corresponding dominant gene, every child will show the recessive trait. (Rare exceptions will be dealt with in later chapters.)

Uncertain odds. There are some genes which may produce particular effects only if they are coupled with unidentified other genes, or only if there are certain special factors in the environment. In such cases the odds for the appearance of the trait in question may be uncertain, and one may speak of inheritance in terms such as "probable," "possible," "not too likely," etc.

▶ *Unexpected results: "beauty" and "homeliness."* It sometimes happens that two very handsome parents will have a child who is definitely not good-looking. If this is not because of some prenatal condition, or some disease, accident, or other environmental factor, heredity may be involved in this way: Each of the good-looking parents could be carrying recessive genes which, coming together in a child, would produce homely features. Fortunately, a much more common situation these days is for two homely parents to have a very good-looking child. This, again, may be for two reasons: 1) Bad environmental conditions in the parents' childhood may have kept them from becoming as good-looking as their genes would have permitted. With more favorable environments today the same genes would make their children better looking. Or, 2) each parent could be carrying genes which in new combinations with the genes from the other parent would produce better looks. (*See accompanying chart.*)

LAWS OF CHANCE. Whenever fractional odds are given that a child or children will or may inherit some trait, the reader

HOW TWO HOMELY PARENTS MAY
HAVE A BEAUTIFUL CHILD

FATHER

MOTHER

Bald

Murky-green
eyes; lashes
lost through
disease

Misshapen
mouth due
to bad
teeth

Bad nose due
to accident

Dull, dark
straight hair

Dull-brown
eyes; droop-
ing eyelids

Bad skin
(local
disorder)

Protruding
under-lip

BUT they may carry and pass
on to their child hidden
genes for

—Blond, curly hair
　Blue eyes
　Long lashes
　Pretty nose
　Cupid's-bow mouth
　Lovely complexion

RESULT: A
"BEAUTY CONTEST"
WINNER

HOW TWO HANDSOME PARENTS MAY
HAVE A HOMELY CHILD

FATHER

MOTHER

Curly, black
hair

Large, dark
eyes, long
lashes

Well-shaped
mouth and
chin

Wavy, blond
hair

Blue eyes,
long lashes

Regular
teeth,
pretty
mouth

BUT they may carry and pass on to
their child hidden genes for

—Dull-brown, straight hair

　Murky-green, small eyes
　with short lashes

　Protruding jaw and
　teeth

　Other irregularities,
　added to by environmental
　factors

RESULT: AN
"UGLY DUCKLING"

(Adapted from an illustration in *The New YOU AND HEREDITY*. Copyright 1939, 1950 by Amram Scheinfeld.)

should bear in mind that these odds are only in terms of averages. The results in the case of a single child or a single family need be no more certain than the results in any game or venture where chance is involved. For instance, if a parent carries a dominant gene for a trait, paired with a recessive gene, the chance that a child will get one or the other is like tossing up a coin. On the average the chances for "heads" or "tails" are exactly even. But sometimes one may get three or four heads in a row, and sometimes a run of tails. Likewise, when we say there is a "fifty-fifty" chance that a child will show a given inherited trait, it is possible in the case of a particular family that this trait may turn up in two or three, or even four children in a row, or in none at all. (This is similar to the situation with regard to the chances of having boys or girls, discussed in Chapter 4.) Again, if we say there is a "one-in-four" chance that a recessive trait may appear, it is possible that in one four-child family, two or three children may have the trait, whereas in another four-child, or even six- or seven-child family, no one will have it.

▶ *How odds remain the same.* One important point which many persons find hard to accept is that the stated odds for the appearance of any trait *remain the same for each successive child* in a family, regardless of what has happened with the others. Again it is like tossing coins: If the chances are fifty-fifty for a head or a tail, one may toss three heads in a row, and there will still be the same fifty-fifty chance that the next toss will bring a head or a tail. So if first-time parents are told there is an even chance they will have a blond baby, and their baby is dark-haired, the chance for their second baby being blond is again no greater or no less than fifty-fifty. Only when one checks the results with large numbers of children does one find that the predicted genetic odds work out very closely.

7
Coloring:
Eyes and Hair

HUMAN COLORING. Human beings are much less gaudily or variably colored than are a great many, if not most, species of other animals; and the human coloring processes are generally simpler. In fact, all the colors of eyes, hair and skin found among human beings of every type and race are produced in much the same way and with the same few basic pigments. The main pigment, or coloring ingredient, is *melanin,* a brownish substance. The amount and strength of this coloring matter, and the way it is distributed, is the chief factor in making eyes, hair or skin darker or lighter. In addition to melanin there are several other pigments which produce special color effects. How the coloring process works in given individuals is determined largely by the activity of the "color" genes they inherit, although various environmental factors can modify the results.

EYE COLOR. This depends mainly on how the basic pigment, melanin, is distributed in the *iris,* the disc-like part of the eye with the pupil at its center. The less pigment there is in the iris, the lighter the eye; the more pigment, the darker. As to particular eye colors, they are not produced by different colored pigments (like painted objects), but are mostly the *effects* of the way the same melanin pigment is concentrated in the eye, and how it reflects the light. In *blue* eyes, for instance, there is no blue pigment in the iris, but the blue effect results only from the way the light is reflected back to the viewer by the pigment particles in the rear of the iris—just as the sky is made to appear blue through an optical effect. In *gray* or *gray-blue* eyes, some extra pigment is distributed in the front of the iris in such a way as to give the grayish effect. In *green* eyes a special scattering of yellow pigment (possibly diluted melanin) in the front of the iris converts the bluish effect into green (somewhat in the way that yellow dots stippled on blue produce a greenish effect). Different amounts of light-brown or yellow pigment in the iris, and different patterns of pigment distribution, produce the various other light eye colors. The darker eyes, ranging from *brown* to *black,* result from the heaviest concentrations of pigment. (See illustration.)

THE "EYE-COLOR" GENES. Although the inheritance of eye color is sometimes complex, the main results usually are determined by a few key genes. A "strong" eye-pigment gene produces dark eyes. "Weak" eye-pigment genes produce the lighter-colored eyes. Should a child receive a "strong" gene from one parent, a "weak" gene from the other, the stronger gene will dominate and the child will have dark eyes (with only occasional exceptions). To have blue eyes, or any other lighter-colored eyes (light gray, light brown, green) a child must therefore get "weaker" color genes from both parents. When the parents have light eyes of different colors, the tendency is for the "blue" gene to be dominated by the "light brown," "gray" or "green" genes, although it is quite possible that the non-blue-eyed parent may also be carrying hidden genes for blue eyes, and that the child will have blue eyes. Some shades and gradations of eye color may be influenced by structural details of the eye, iris patterns, blood vessels in the eye, chemical influences in the body and the state of the person's health.

▶ *Albino eyes.* True albino eyes have no pigment in them whatsoever. The "pinkness" of these eyes results from the tiny blood vessels in the otherwise colorless iris, and the reflection from other blood vessels inside the eye. The absence of eye pigment is due to a pair of abnormal genes which also interfere with the coloring processes of the hair and skin. (Further details on albinism and its inheritance in later chapters. See Index.)

▶ *Unmatched eyes.* In occasional instances a person may have one eye dark and the other light, or each eye of a different shade or color. This condition (*heterochromia iridis*) may result in several ways, and sometimes heredity may be involved. For example: 1) A person may inherit one brown-eye gene and one blue-eye gene. Normally this would produce brown eyes; but if in an early embryonic stage the brown-eye gene is knocked out of action on one side of the face, the blue-eye gene may take over on that side, producing a blue eye, whereas the other eye with its brown gene working as usual becomes brown. 2) In an embryo with light-eye genes something may happen to increase pigment production abnormally in one of the eyes, causing it to become much darker, or different in color, from the other. 3) While either of the foregoing situations may be purely environmental, it is also possible for an inherited abnormality to produce

Eye Colors

*All eye colors are effects of how genes work
to produce pigment deposits in the iris*

BLUE EYES

Light deposit of pigment in rear of iris, but not in front. "Blue" is only an optical effect. (See text.)

GRAY EYES

Light pigmentation in rear, as in blue eyes, but also some scattered dark pigment in front, which "grays down" the blue effect.

GREEN EYES

Rear of iris pigmented as in blue eyes, but scattered yellow pigment in front: Yellow over blue effect gives the green hue.

BROWN EYES

Heavy deposit of pigment in rear of iris, and also some pigment in front.

BLACK EYES

Very heavy deposit of pigment in both rear and front of the iris.

ALBINO EYES

No pigment at all in iris —"pink" effect due to reflection of blood vessels inside.

unmatched eyes. The condition, either dominant or recessive, runs in some human families, but is much more common among cats, dogs, rabbits and other animals.

▶ *Rare eye colors.* "Tortoise-shell" eyes (mottled yellow and black) and "ruby" eyes are among rare types found in individuals. They may possibly occur through mutations in the eye-color genes.

Changes in Eye Color. While most persons' eyes remain the same in basic color throughout life, it should not be overlooked that eye colors are capable of being modified by inherent chemical changes, aging effects and various environmental factors. At birth most White babies (and many Negro babies) have slate-blue eyes, which in some may presently become heavily pigmented, turning brown, and in others may turn clear blue, depending on the types of genes they received. Sometimes a child's true eye color does not become set until it is several years old, and often there is a change at puberty. Diseases or nutritional deficiencies may affect eye-pigment production, leading to either darkening or lightening. Cataracts may make dark eyes bluish, as may aging effects.

PREDICTING CHILDREN'S EYE COLORS. The facts given in preceding sections, and in those which follow, should enable most prospective parents to make fairly accurate guesses as to what the eye colors of their children will be—or, at least, what the odds are that given types of eye color will appear in them.

▶ *Both parents dark-eyed.* All children will have dark eyes— *unless each mate* has some light-eyed close blood relative (particularly one of his or her parents, or a brother or sister), in which case there is a chance (but no more than one in four) of having a light-eyed child (blue, gray or green-eyed). Only rarely do two dark-eyed parents with no known light-eyed blood relatives produce a light-eyed child, but it can happen. Once two dark-eyed parents have had a light-eyed child, there is a one-in-four chance of having another or others.

▶ *One mate dark-eyed, the other light-eyed.* If the dark-eyed mate has no light-eyed close blood relative, there is little more chance of the couple's having a light-eyed child than if both mates are dark-eyed. (See preceding section.) But if the dark-eyed mate does have one or more light-eyed relatives (particularly a parent) there is up to a one-in-two chance of producing a light-eyed child or children in conjunction with the light-eyed mate.

▶ *Both mates light-eyed.* It is about 98 per cent certain each is carrying only light-eye genes, and that all their children will be light-eyed. Should both mates be blue-eyed, their children will have approximately the same eye color. But if the eyes of one or both parents are green, gray or very light brown, a child's eyes may be any one of these colors, or blue. But no child's eyes in a mating between two light-eyed parents are apt to be much darker than the eyes of either parent. However, in about 2 per cent of the cases this may happen if one of the parents is carrying a hidden "dark-eye" gene which for some complex reason failed to assert itself. (The fact that a wife and husband are blue-eyed, and that a dark-eyed child is born to them, is therefore by no means proof that the child is not legitimate. See "Disputed Parentage Cases," Chap. 28.)

HAIR-COLOR INHERITANCE. This follows the same principles as in eye-color inheritance. The degrees of darkness in hair depend on how "strong" or active the hair-pigment genes are, mainly with respect to how much of the basic brown pigment, *melanin,* they produce. In black hair the hair cells are heavily filled with melanin; in brown hair there is less; in light, blond hair there is very little; and in white hair virtually none. Special hair-color effects may result from the addition of other pigments (as in red hair). Shades of the same hair color may be influenced by the way the hair cells are constructed, their oiliness or dryness, changes in the body chemistry, and other factors, in all of which hereditary tendencies, as well as environmental influences, play a part. In children light hair tends to darken somewhat with puberty, blond hair often becoming brown; while in later ages, of course, hair may become lighter through the weakened action of the pigment genes and changes in the hair cells. (Natural gray hair, and premature gray hair, are due to special factors to be discussed later.) All of the various influences on hair color must be taken into account in tracing hair-color inheritance in any family.

The "Hair-Color" Genes

All human hair-color differences are due mainly to how genes work to deposit the basic brownish pigment, melanin, *among the hair cells*

BLOND HAIR

Dilute melanin pigment gives yellowish effect. The less the pigment, the lighter the shade of blond.

RED HAIR

A special gene works to produce red pigment, diffused with scattered *melanin* pigment.

BROWN HAIR

Heavy deposit of pigment. The more pigment, the darker the shade of brown.

BLACK HAIR

Extremely heavy deposit of melanin-pigment granules.

NOTE: Various internal and external influences can modify the effects of the "hair-color" genes. See text.

(Adapted from *The New* YOU AND HEREDITY. Copyright, 1939, 1950, by Amram Scheinfeld.)

The Hair-Color Genes. As is also true in eye color, the strongest and most active hair-color genes almost always dominate the weaker ones, so that if a person inherits a dark-hair gene from one parent, a light-hair gene from the other, the hair will be dark. For the same reason, a dark-haired person may often be carrying a hidden gene for any of the lighter hair shades, but a fair-haired person cannot be carrying a dark-hair gene (except in rare instances).

▶ *Red hair* results from special genes, which produce a reddish pigment. The degree to which the red shows through depends on the activity of the other hair-color genes the person carries. When coupled with a gene for black hair, the effects of the "red" gene will be obscured. But when the red-hair gene is coupled with genes for lighter hair shades, the results may be reddish-gold, chestnut, or vividly red hair. The red-hair genes are found in all racial groups, including pure Negroes, among whom red hair sometimes appears when their dark-hair genes are not strongly active. (See also last paragraph of this chapter.)

▶ *White hair.* This can be due to several causes: 1) Defective genes (as in albinos) which prevent the production of any pigment in the hair cells; 2) very weak blond-hair genes, which produce almost no pigment; 3) diseases, hereditary or environmental, which interfere with the hair-pigmenting process; or 4) aging effects. In the latter case, the approximate stage in a person's life when his hair begins to gray and then turns white is often governed by heredity, with the graying taking place in some families much earlier than others. While nerve disorders, diseases or shocks may affect hair cells and the hair-pigmentation process, causing new hair to grow out white, it is a myth that a person's whole head of hair can turn white "overnight."

▶ *Eye and hair color.* In most cases very dark eyes and very dark hair go together, almost invariably so among pure Negroes and Mongolians. But among Whites it is not uncommon to see a person with very dark hair and blue or light-gray eyes, or, conversely, blond hair and dark eyes. Among Mulattoes and other racially mixed persons, also, dark-light combinations in eyes and hair (or vice versa) are seen. This is proof that the eye-color and hair-color genes may be inherited separately and work independently.

FORECASTING CHILDREN'S HAIR COLOR. In trying to guess what an expected child's hair color will be, parents must first seek to determine what hair-color genes they carry. They can be guided in this by being clear as to the *natural* color of their hair, ruling out any changes produced artificially or by acquired diseases (which can have had no effect on their genes); by what their own hair color was in childhood and at puberty; and by types and shades of hair color in their parents, brothers and sisters, and other close relatives. With these facts in mind, the following general forecasts may be made:

▶ *Both parents dark-haired.* All children will have dark hair —*unless each parent* has some light-haired close blood relative or relatives (or is otherwise carrying a hidden "light-hair" gene), in which case there is a chance—but no more than one in four —of having a light-haired child. In any case once a dark-haired couple has had a fair-haired child, there is a one-in-four chance of having another or others.

▶ *One mate dark-haired, other light-haired.* If the dark-haired mate has no light-haired close blood relative, which strongly indicates he or she is carrying only "dark-hair" genes, there is little more chance of the couple's having a light-haired child than if both parents were dark-haired. (See preceding section.) But if the dark-haired mate does have one or more fair-haired close relatives (particularly a parent), there is up to a one-in-two chance of producing a fair-haired child in conjunction with the light-haired mate.

▶ *Both parents brown-haired.* Most children's hair will be brown, possibly a little darker or lighter than the parents', and with a chance that some child may be blond.

▶ *Both parents blond.* Their children are almost certain to be blond (especially if the parents are light blond or flaxen-haired). But occasionally blond parents may produce a brown-haired child.

▶ *Red hair.* Two true red-headed parents are likely to have all red-headed children, but light-brown or blond hair may also appear among their offspring. If one mate is red-headed, the other blond, there may be an even chance of having a red-headed child, with a reduced chance if the other parent is dark-haired. Redheads also appear sometimes when both mates are dark-haired, but only very rarely if both parents are blond.

8

Skin Color

HUMAN DIFFERENCES. While there are marked differences in skin color among individuals—especially of different races—we noted in the last chapter that all human beings have the same basic skin-coloring elements, although in varying proportions as governed by particular genes. *Melanin* is the chief skin-coloring pigment, as it is in eye and hair coloring. There are several additional skin pigments, among them *melanoid* and *carotene* (yellowish or yellowish-red), and several blood pigments in the skin which contribute to its coloring. Also influencing the skin color of individuals is the structure of the skin and its thickness and oiliness, to which heredity may contribute. Environment can modify skin color through such factors as exposure to the sun (to be discussed later), changes in the person's health, and age. But since the effects of environment cannot be inherited, the big differences in human coloring everywhere are those produced by the genes people inherit.

THE SKIN-COLOR GENES. What chiefly determines a person's skin color is the way that certain genes work to lay down deposits of the two brownish pigments, melanin and melanoid, in the skin cells. The relative amounts and strengths of these pigments, and how they are combined in persons, account for many grades of skin color, from almost black through dark brown, light brown and light. In other words, the most active "melanin-melanoid" genes are in the darkest Negroes, the least active in the "whitest" Whites. In addition, an especially active "carotene" gene contributes to the yellowish skin of Mongolians and the bronze skin of their relatives, the American Indians. However, the terms "Black," "Yellow," "Red," and "White" to describe races are highly inexact, because few Negroes are really black, no Mongolians are really yellow, no Indians are red, and no Whites are white. But more than this, some Whites, such as are found in India and the Arab countries, have blacker skins than many Negroes (even of certain native African tribes).

▶ *Skin-Color mixtures.* In offspring of persons with markedly different skin colors there may appear to be a "blending" of the colors, but actually, the effects are only those of new combinations of the skin-color genes. There is an important difference here from the way the eye-color or hair-color genes work. In producing eye color, if a dark-eye gene is coupled with a light-eye gene, the dark-eye gene dominates the process (as we saw in the preceding chapter), and the child has dark eyes. The results with one dark-eye gene are the same as with two dark-eye genes. (This is also true of combined dark and light hair-color genes.) But in skin color, if one dark-skin gene is coupled with one light-skin gene, there is no dominance of the first over the second. Instead there is an in-between result.

▶ *Negro-White matings.* How the skin-color genes work is best shown in the results of (a), a Negro-White mating, producing Mulatto offspring; and (b), a mating between two Mulattoes. As indicated in the accompanying illustration, a pure Negro carries several pairs of "dark-skin" genes and a pure White several pairs of "white-skin" genes. (There are probably more than the two pairs shown for each.) In the first mating, each of the offspring receives one set of the "Negro-skin" genes, and one set of the "white-skin" genes, which produces in each much the same in-between skin color. But when two Mulattoes mate, their different skin-color genes sort out independently to form any of various combinations: One child may get *all* "Negro-skin" genes, and be as dark as the darkest Negro grandparent; another child may get *all* "white-skin" genes, and be as light as the lightest White grandparent; or a child may get any mixed combination of the genes, and have any skin color in between these extremes. However, since the "feature" genes (which we will deal with in the next chapter) are also inherited separately, a child of two Mulattoes who has the lightest skin might have features which are much more Negroid than those of his darkest brother.

Skin Color

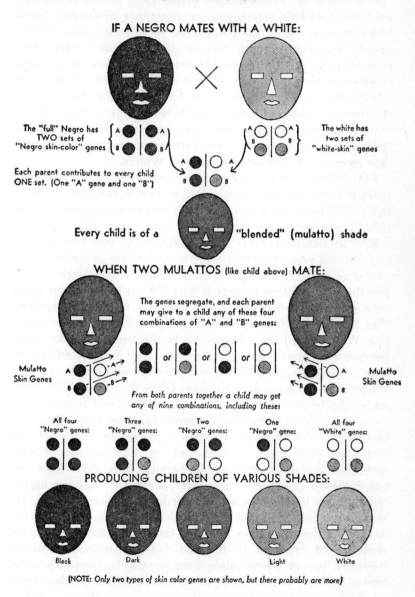

IF A NEGRO MATES WITH A WHITE:

The "full" Negro has TWO sets of "Negro skin-color" genes

The white has two sets of "white-skin" genes

Each parent contributes to every child ONE set. (One "A" gene and one "B")

Every child is of a "blended" (mulatto) shade

WHEN TWO MULATTOS (like child above) MATE:

The genes segregate, and each parent may give to a child any of these four combinations of "A" and "B" genes:

or   or   or

Mulatto Skin Genes

Mulatto Skin Genes

From both parents together a child may get any of nine combinations, including these:

All four "Negro" genes:

Three "Negro" genes:

Two "Negro" genes:

One "Negro" gene:

All four "White" genes:

PRODUCING CHILDREN OF VARIOUS SHADES:

Black   Dark   Light   White

(NOTE: Only two types of skin color genes are shown, but there probably are more)

(Adapted from *The New YOU AND HEREDITY*. Copyright, 1939, 1950, by Amram Scheinfeld.)

▶ *"Throwback" children.* One of the most persistent popular myths is that two White parents sometimes produce a "coal-black" baby if one of the parents has some long-hidden "Negro blood." This cannot really happen, first, because a very dark-skinned baby can be produced only if it receives Negro skin-color genes from *both* parents; and second, if one parent alone carried skin-color genes strong enough to make the baby "black," that parent would not look White. Wherever these "black-baby" cases have been tracked down, they are either found to be un-true, or else the parents involved were both racially mixed and may or may not have been passing as Whites.

▶ *American Negro-White mixing.* Contrary to popular notions, there is probably less Negro-White mixing in the United States today than in former times, and the Negro population as a whole is not becoming lighter in skin color. (See Chap. 27.)

ENVIRONMENT AND SKIN COLOR. All that environment can do with respect to skin color is to increase or decrease the *effects* of the skin-color genes to a certain extent. Under a hot sun the pigmentation process is speeded up to lay down more pigment particles in the skin and thus give it added protection. This is what happens when a person tans during the summer. If a White man lives a long time in the tropics his skin may become very tanned, but no matter how dark it gets it will never look like true Negro skin. Nor will his children be born any less White than if he lived in Norway. Once the same White man leaves the tropics and remains away his skin will become pro-gressively lighter. Pure Negroes, however, have much the same basic skin color whether they live in Africa or in the United States, although those exposed continually to hot sun will be somewhat darker, everything else equal, than those who are not. But even in Africa, as elsewhere, under the same conditions some strains of Negroes are always much darker than others. Nor need it be added that the dark skin of Negroes is due solely to the fact that they have inherited dark-skin genes, and not to centuries of exposure to the sun (as Shakespeare's Othello thought). Just as White children continue to be born to heavily tanned White parents in the tropics, dark Negro children continue to be born to Negroes who for generations have lived in northern American cities.

▶ *Sunburn.* Heredity plays a considerable part in the way different skins react to the sun. In some White persons the pigment genes will be quickly stirred to added activity under a hot sun, and they will tan easily and with no discomfort. Other persons—particularly fair-skinned redheads and those with "milky-white" skins—will simply *broil*. But even some Negroes sunburn painfully.

PREDICTING CHILDREN'S SKIN COLORS. Because of the complexity of skin-color inheritance, only a few general observations can be made other than those with respect to Negro-White or Mulatto matings. Among Whites, where one parent has darkish, swarthy skin (as in Italians, Arabians and other Mediterranean peoples) and the other parent is fair-skinned, the children are likely to be of in-between shades. Again, if both parents are of mixed stock, each with some swarthy and some fair-skinned relatives, their children may also be any of these varied skin-color types. Familial resemblances in skin color are apt to become stronger with aging.

▶ *Freckles.* The tendency to freckling often runs in families, with inheritance by way of a *dominant* gene. Transmission of freckling is especially likely where there is also red hair.

▶ *Albino skin color.* See Chap. 13.

9

The Features

ONE'S PHYSICAL "LOOKS." Many things can make people look the way they do. Heredity, obviously, is almost the sole factor in making humans distinctive in every detail of their looks from all other animals. But it is the relatively minor differences in appearance among humans themselves which we have in mind when we speak of inheritance of features. As a rule, then, the genes set the pattern for the way individual characteristics in features develop in the growing child, the shapes they take at maturity, and the changes they undergo in later years. One of the clearest proofs of this is that identical twins, who have the same genes, usually preserve a remarkable resemblance to each other throughout life, even when living apart under different conditions. However, environment can often do a great deal to modify the features, although much more, usually, with respect to their outer forms than to their inner construction. The changes in underlying fat, tissue and muscles of the face and its parts are what we chiefly notice when we remark upon the differences in a person's looks that result from disease, state of health or age.

▶ *The "feature" genes.* There are a great many of these which work together to shape both the face as a whole and its separate details. For instance, the shaping and appearance of the eyes will depend not only on the specific "eye" genes, but on the way other genes help to construct the brows, forehead, nose bridge, and cheekbones, and to lay down fatty tissue in the region. Other features are similarly influenced in their appearance by surrounding details.

▶ *Sex differences.* Although men and women inherit the same "feature" genes, the effects of these may be considerably modified in one direction or another by basic sex differences in body

58

chemistry. Thus, just as the "XY" and "XX" sex-chromosome
mechanisms cause the sex organs of males to develop differently
from those of females, in a more limited way they also affect
the features, causing males as a group to have relatively heavier
brows, squarer chins, heavier facial muscles and more facial and
body hair, and women to have softer facial contours and relatively smaller noses, ears and mouths. (For sex differences in
stature and body form, see next chapter.)

THE EYES. Shapes and appearances of persons' eyes result
mainly from the way the key eye genes construct the eye sockets,
eyeballs and eyelids, as well as the surrounding bony structures
of the face and their fleshy parts. Moreover, the width of the
nose bridge has an important influence on the spacing between
the eyes.

"Eye-Shape" Genes

STRAIGHT EYES   **MONGOLIAN EYES**   **SLANT EYES**

Note contrast between true slant eyes and the Mongolian, which
only appear slanted because of overlapping inner eyelid fold
(*epicanthus*). When mixed eye-shape genes are inherited, the
gene for Mongolian dominates the straight-eye and slant-eye
genes of Whites; the straight-eye gene in turn dominates the
slant-eye. (See text.)

▶ *Mongolian and "slant" eyes.* The distinctive inherited eye
shapes of the Mongolians (Chinese, Japanese, Eskimos, etc.)
result from fatty underpadding of the lids, and thick folds
(*epicanthic*) overlapping the inner corners, giving the eyes al-
mond-shape, or oblique effects. Mongolian eyes should not be
confused with the true "slant" eyes found among Whites and
other peoples, in which the inner skin folds are absent and the
eyes really slant upward toward the outer corners. Moreover,
the genes for the two types of eyes work differently, the genes

for Mongolian eyes being dominant, those for true slant eyes recessive. Thus, in matings between a Mongolian and a White, the children will almost always have Mongolian eyes. But if in two White parents one has slant eyes, the other straight eyes, the children are likely to have straight eyes.

▶ *Other eye-gene workings.* Wide or large eyes: The genes tend to be dominant. If one parent's eyes are wide and/or large, the other parent's narrow and/or small, their children will tend to have the wide or large eyes. (*Abnormally small eyes:* See "Eye Defects," Chap. 14.)

▶ *Deep-set eyes.* Genes usually recessive. If only one parent has such eyes, the child is not too likely to have them.

▶ *Long lashes.* Dominant. If one parent has them, they are likely to reappear in a child.

▶ *Drooping eyelids.* A dominant abnormality. (See Chap. 14.)

THE NOSE. While one hears it said, "He has his father's nose," etc., this organ is not inherited as a unit. Its shape and size result from the action of a number of separate genes, governing the sizes and forms of its different parts—the bridge, nostrils, "bulb" or tip, and the junction with the upper lip. If a person does have a nose which seems almost a replica of that of one parent, it is likely he received a combination of the "nose" genes from the parent which dominated those from the other parent. More often a child's nose will resemble that of one parent in only one or two main details, while also showing some characteristics of the other parent's nose. But in all cases due allowance should be made for aging effects and environmental influences on nose shapes. In addition to radical changes in nose shapes at puberty, less perceptible and gradual changes may occur through the years as part of the normal maturing and aging processes. Often family resemblances in noses become most evident in the older years. On the other hand, hereditary nose characteristics may be masked or canceled out in individuals by accidents, diseases, plastic operations, effects of abnormal diet or heavy drinking, and other environmental factors. All the foregoing facts must be taken into account when tracing inheritance of nose shapes in any family.

▶ *Nose inheritance predictions.* If two parents have very different nose shapes—one straight and moderate-sized, the other prominent, hooked, high-bridged, humped or pug-nosed—the genes for the more prominent or extreme details usually dominate, and these tend to reappear in a child. If both parents have rather small, straight, regular noses, the children all are apt to have noses of the same type. However, since the various "nose" genes may sort out and work independently, one child in a family may have a small nose with large nostrils, another a long nose with small nostrils. Varieties of noses may be found especially in offspring of two Mulatto parents who carry both White and Negro nose genes. In matings between Whites and Negroes, the children's noses tend to have the high and narrow bridges of the White parents and the broad nostrils of the Negro parents.

MOUTH AND TEETH. Inheritance of mouth shapes may be even more complex than of nose shapes. Not only is the mouth much influenced by the structure of the jaws, teeth, palate, and surrounding muscles, but being so movable and in such constant use, its form and appearance are continually and throughout life affected by the person's talking, eating and sleeping habits, facial expressions and moods. In addition, there are the marked changes in mouth shape that illness and aging can produce. Hereditary factors in mouth shapes can therefore be identified only after environmental influences are ruled out, and this is not easy. To date conclusions have been arrived at only with respect to the more marked racial differences and a few odd or abnormal conditions.

▶ *Negro and White lips.* In mixed matings, the genes for the thick Negro lips tend to dominate. If the Negro parent has no White genes, the offspring are all likely to have thick lips. In matings between Mulattoes, the offspring may have various types of lips and mouths, showing that a considerable number of different genes are involved.

▶ *"Hapsburg" lip.* This peculiarity of a protruding lower lip, usually with a narrow, undershot jaw, is named after the royal Spanish and Austrian families in which it has been prevalent for generations. It is dominant in inheritance.

▶ *Dimples.* Usually dominant. If in one parent, a child is likely to have dimples.

▶ *Chins.* Receding chins tend usually to be recessive to straight; narrow or pointed chins recessive to wide chins. In matings between parents with these different chin shapes, the children are more likely to have straight rather than receding chins, and wide rather than narrow or pointed chins.

▶ *Teeth.* There are marked family tendencies toward various types of teeth and the manner in which upper and lower teeth are set together. But eating habits, diet, tooth care and other conditions may also contribute to these family resemblances. Where direct evidence of inheritance in teeth can best be seen is in the abnormal conditions described in Chapter 13.

HAIR FORM. Natural differences in hair form, from curly to poker-straight, are determined chiefly by the way genes cause the hair to be shaped and to grow out of the hair follicles in the scalp. The genes for the frizziest or curliest types of hair usually dominate those for straighter hair. Most potent is the "woolly" gene, found largely among Negroes, but sometimes also, though rarely, in Whites who have no Negro blood. Next in order of potency, the "kinky" gene dominates the ordinary "curly"; the "curly" dominates the "wavy"; the "wavy" dominates the ordinary "straight." However, the very thick, straight Mongolian hair is of a special type, and the gene for this may dominate all the others. Thus, in matings between pure Mongolians and Whites, and usually between Mongolians and Negroes, the offspring will all have the thick, straight hair. Likewise, in matings between White persons and Negroes with woolly hair, the Negro type of hair will tend to appear in offspring.

Hair inheritance in Whites. Ruling out any artificial changes made in parents' hair, and keeping in mind that hair form may change with age—wavy or curly hair often becoming straighter— here are some predictions of what a child's hair form will be:

▶ *Curly hair.* A child has little likelihood of being curly-haired unless at least one parent has natural curly hair. If both parents are curly-haired, the chances of the child's being so increase and become almost certain if all of the parents' close relatives are curly-haired. Should there be relatives with wavy hair and/or straight hair, these hair types may also appear in children of curly-haired parents, though with less frequency than curly hair.

▶ *Wavy hair.* A child with such hair results most often if both parents are wavy-haired, or if one parent and all of his or her close relatives are the same. If one parent has wavy hair, the other straight, the chances are even for either type to appear in a child.

▶ *Straight hair.* If in both parents, their children are almost certain all to have straight hair.

▶ *Kinky hair.* If just one parent is kinky-headed, and comes from a family with that hair type, the children are all likely to be kinky-haired. But if the one parent has some non-kinky-haired relatives and the other parent has curly, wavy or straight hair, there is an even chance any of their children's hair will not be kinky.

The "Hair-Form" Genes

One's inherited hair form depends on how genes work to shape the hairs and the follicles out of which they grow

STRAIGHT HAIR
(Caucasian)

Follicle

Round in cross-section (like a pipe). Follicle straight.

CURLY
OR WAVY

Oval cross-section (curly hair more oval, wavy less so). Hair twisted. Follicle curved.

KINKY
OR WOOLLY

Flat oval cross-section. Hair twisted, pinched. Follicle curved.

(For inheritance workings, see text.)

Hairiness. The tendency to have much or little hair on the head or body, or both, is strongly influenced by heredity. Race differences offer the best examples. Mongolians (especially full-blooded American Indians) have the least facial and body hair, Negroes have more, and Whites have the most. The hairiest of all peoples are the primitive Ainus of Japan, who are of White origins.

▶ *Heavy eyebrows* growing together are most common in Greeks, Turks, Armenians, and other Mediterranean peoples, but also are sometimes found in other groups, including the Irish and Welsh. Apart from the gene workings, hormonal factors may have much to do with the extent of hair growth on the face or body. The most marked differences in this respect are between women and men, with the male sex hormones tending to stimulate such hair growth.

▶ *Baldness:* See special discussion in Chapter 13.

10

Shape and Stature

HUMAN SIZES. The general sizes of all human beings, as of animals of other species, are determined by their heredity. The human genes dictate that no person can grow to be as big as an elephant, nor as small as a mouse. Moreover, human "stature" genes work within a much narrower range than do those of many other species: For example, there are no such size differences among human beings as among dogs—a giant Saint Bernard or a pint-sized Mexican Chihuahua. It is because the differences in human stature are so limited that we often attach such importance to a few inches more or less in height. At the same time, the limited differences have made it difficult to study stature inheritance, with added complications resulting from the fact that the influences of environment on stature must always be taken into account.

▶ *Biggest and littlest.* In terms of groups, the very tallest human beings today are African Negroes of the Lake Chad tribes, near the lower Nile, whose males average 6 feet 1 inch in height, with many 7 feet and over. (These were the towering Negroes shown in the movie, *King Solomon's Mines.*) The smallest humans are the pygmy Negrillos, also of Africa, whose adult males average 4 feet 6 inches. (Midgets and giants are in the abnormal category. See Chap. 13.) Apart from these extremes the differences between peoples of stocks we call "tall," such as the Swedes, and those we call "short," such as the Japanese or Italians, may be a matter of only two or three inches on the average. The principal reasons why the stature differences of the various human ethnic stocks are not greater is that there has been constant interbreeding among them, and that no attempt was ever made to breed human groups deliberately for tallness or shortness.

▶ *Sex differences.* In any group and under any conditions, a major factor in determining height is an individual's sex. Given exactly the same "stature" genes, a male will grow about 6 per cent taller than a female, or somewhat over three quarters of an inch more to each foot of her size. Thus, among Americans at this writing, men average just above 5 feet 8 inches (174 cm.), women 5 feet 4 inches (164 cm.). This difference can be little more attributed to environmental factors, such as work activities, diet, living habits, etc., than can the differences in size between bulls and cows, or roosters and hens. Obviously, the internal chemical differences between the sexes, set in motion by their respective "XX" and "XY" chromosome mechanisms, cause their skeletal and bodily developments to diverge not only in size, but in proportions. (Further discussion under "Sex Differences in Body Form.") But this indicates that in individuals of either sex, special internal chemical factors may also modify the activity of their "stature" genes and the development of their bodily details. Some of these factors may be hereditary, some environmental, and some a combination of the two. (For extreme examples, see "Stature Abnormalities," Chapter 13.)

▶ *Environment and stature.* Just as plants and flowers grow taller if they are in good soil and are properly watered and tended, or can be stunted if conditions are poor, so the statures of human beings also can be considerably influenced by their environments. Although human genes have changed little in thousands of years, people of modern times are considerably taller than were those of ancient and medieval periods. Most noticeable have been the changes in the past half century, with the new generations of Americans being taller than their grandparents by an average of about two inches. Especially marked increases are among offspring of various immigrant stocks, with frequent cases of sons four to six inches taller than their fathers. In most European countries, and in many other advanced countries, including Japan, increases in stature have also been noted. For the most part this increase has been attributed to great improvements in diet, living conditions and medical care. However, some scientists believe that changes in the earth's climate, and in meteorological and cosmic conditions, have added to the stature increase.

▶ *How much taller can people grow?* Many experts think that in about two hundred years more the average height of American males will be at least 6 feet, with a great many up to 7 feet or somewhat over, while the average American woman will be about as tall as the average man now is. Any much greater height may bring difficulties. As will be noted in Chapter 13, giants of 8 feet or over have tended to be weak, glandular cases, usually short-lived.

FAMILIAL STATURE INHERITANCE. Whatever the environmental conditions may be anywhere, it is evident that tendencies toward greater height run in some families, and toward lesser height in others. How the "stature" genes work is not precisely known, but as a rule it appears that the "shortness" genes dominate the "tallness" genes. This means that a tall person probably is not carrying any "shortness" genes, and that if two tall persons mate, all their children will be tall, except in individual cases where diseases, dietary deficiencies, hormonal upsets, etc., may stunt normal growth. Short persons may or may not be carrying hidden "tallness" genes; they probably are not if they are of short stocks on both sides and if this shortness was not due to environmental factors. But if they had or have some close relatives who are tall, they may very well be carrying hidden genes for tallness, and may produce children much taller than themselves. This is especially likely to be so with persons who had grown up under unfavorable conditions, as with those of various immigrant groups. (See preceding sections.) Where one parent is genetically short, and the other tall, the odds are somewhat greater that the children will be short rather than tall.

▶ *Age changes in stature.* In judging inheritance of stature, or drawing conclusions with respect to individuals, full allowance should be made for age changes that have taken place or may take place, and for the fact that different individuals have different growth rates, even with the same stature genes. Males sometimes do not reach their full height until age twenty-three or twenty-four, females not until twenty-one or twenty-two.

Some shrinkage in height in men and women may begin to occur as early as age thirty, becoming more pronounced with added years, so that by age seventy a man may be about one inch or more shorter than he was at twenty-five.

BODY FORM. While skeletal structure is largely determined by heredity, as is stature, a person's "upholstery"—the muscles, fat and outer tissues—can be strongly influenced by environment. Thus, where an individual's height remains almost the same from maturity on (except for the slight decline with aging, just noted), the outer body form may change frequently, and sometimes radically within a short time. Moreover, occupations and living habits can do much to influence the structure and outer form of the body or its parts, as is shown in certain bodily characteristics common to farmers, sailors, dancers, etc. Such environmental characteristics may be mistaken for inherited traits when they appear in successive members of families who have worked at the same tasks for generations. Nevertheless, with full allowance for the environmental influences, definite tendencies toward given proportions and details of the body are strongly conditioned by a person's genetic makeup.

▶ *Obesity.* This bodily characteristic has received much attention in the current period when so many people are weight-conscious. Although many complex factors, both physical and psychological, are generally involved in obesity, there is evidence that tendencies toward fatness or slenderness may have an hereditary basis. In lower animals some strains of a species have been bred which are excessively fat, others lean. Also, in human beings, studies of twins show that obesity is far more often a common trait of both members of an identical pair than of a fraternal pair, or of non-twin siblings. "Obesity" genes, it is believed, work mainly through the glands, causing certain individuals to put on much more fat per pound of food consumed than do others, or increasing the proportion of weight gain that is fatty tissue. This does not mean that even glandular obesity is always, or most often, due to heredity, since many of these cases are traceable to acquired diseases. (See "Extreme Fatness," Chap. 13.) Further, when all members of a family are fat it may often be because of their similar diets and ways of living. But when environmental causes are minimal, genetic studies indicate that a predisposition toward obesity may be produced by *dominant* genes, with tendencies toward leanness produced by *recessive* genes. Thus, on this basis, slender parents, carrying no "obesity" genes, will usually have only slender children. But fat parents, while tending to have fat children, may be carrying hidden "slimness" genes, and so may also have some slender children.

SEX DIFFERENCES IN BODY FORM. Whatever the special effects of "body-form" genes may be, a most important fact is that their general workings are very different in males and females. Just as the same "stature" genes produce greater height in the male than the female, the same "body-form" genes, as in a brother and sister, have divergent effects on almost every detail of their skeletal structure and fleshy parts. In the male the bones are relatively thicker and heavier, as are the muscles; the chest is larger and broader; the hands and feet are longer, blunter and heavier. (Skull differences between males and females, as affecting their features, were described in the preceding chapter.) In the female the shoulders are relatively narrower and more sloping; and the hips are wider and bigger, because the hip structure is both broader than in the males, and covered with more fat. The extra fatty layers found in females, as a rule, in addition to their softer muscles, contribute toward making their contours more rounded than those of the male. A seldom-noted sex difference is in the alignment of the arm and leg bones: In the male the upper and lower arms are usually in line when the arm is held straightened out against the side, whereas in the female the lower arm tends to jut out from the elbow. (Illustration, p. 71) Also, females tend to be more knock-kneed, in part because their hips are wider and their thighs heavier.

▶ *Breast shapes.* Different sizes and shapes of breasts in women may result from different types of "breast" genes, although diet, health factors, physical activities and childbearing and nursing are modifying influences. Some of the most striking hereditary breast types are found in women of certain African tribes. The genes for any type of female breasts, it should be noted, can be transmitted as easily through the father as through the mother.

This explains why, in many cases, a mother may note that a grown daughter has distinctive breasts not like hers, but like those of the husband's mother or one of his sisters. (A son, similarly, can inherit through his mother, male bodily traits which are like those of her male relatives rather than his father's.)

▶ *Glandular factors.* Much of the work of the "sex" genes in shaping bodily details in either "male" or "female" directions is carried out through the way they construct and influence the sex glands—the testes in the male, ovaries in the female. This is shown by what happens if these glands are removed, or if the production of their normal quotas of "male" and "female" hormones is radically changed. If a male is castrated before he achieves puberty, his body will develop many of the feminine characteristics (wider hips, soft muscles, lack of facial hair, etc.). If the sex glands in a young woman do not function properly before or during puberty (or if they are removed through operation as is sometimes necessary), her breasts, hips and contours may not develop in the normal female way. Often in these cases a girl may also grow unusually tall. (Proper medical treatment given in time, with the supplement of the required sex hormones, may help to prevent or correct these deviations from normal body development.) However, if the glandular changes or upsets occur *after* puberty, when the skeletal structure is set, the effects on the outward sex characteristics are much less. Castration of an adult male will in time make him flabbier and fattier in his tissues; but in a woman, removal of the ovaries after maturity usually has very little outward effect.

HEAD SHAPES. Whether a person is roundheaded (*brachycephalic*), or longheaded (*dolichocephalic*) in maturity depends largely on heredity, but diet and living conditions are modifying influences. While all shapes of heads are found among all peoples, round heads (broad oval) predominate among the Mongolians, long heads (long oval) among Negroes. Among Whites one head shape may be more prevalent in some groups, another head shape in other groups. As a rule, if parents have different head shapes, the "roundhead" genes tend to dominate those for long heads. But any predictions of head-shape inheritance should take into consideration environmental influences. For instance, stature has a relationship to head shape, since a lengthening of the body bones may also bring a lengthening of the skull. Thus, the increase in stature in the United States has brought some lengthening of heads, and particularly in immigrant stocks offspring may have head shapes somewhat different from their parents.

Sex Characteristics in Limbs

ARMS

FEMALES	MALES
Angle, corresponding to knock-knees	Straight

LOWER LIMBS

FEMALES	MALES
Slightly knock-kneed	Straight

ANGLE

STRAIGHT

(From The New YOU AND HEREDITY. Copyright 1939, 1950 by Amram Scheinfeld.)

Other bodily details. Inherited factors in shapes of hands, feet, chests, muscles, etc., have been studied mainly with respect to abnormal traits, to be discussed in Chapter 13. But here are two recently reported "normal" oddities:

▶ *"Hitch-hiker's thumb."* Double-jointed thumbs, capable of being bent back at an angle of 50 degrees or more, are inherited through simple recessive genes. The condition occurs in about one in four Whites and one in three Negroes, with one thumb affected in 60 per cent of these individuals, both thumbs in 40 per cent. (Reported by Dr. H. Bentley Glass.)

▶ *Index and ring finger lengths.* An interesting sex difference, reported by Dr. V. Rae Phelps, is that the majority of women, but only a quarter of men, have index fingers markedly longer than ring fingers, whereas the majority of men, compared with only 30 per cent of women, have index fingers shorter than ring fingers. The finger-length differences are believed hereditary, with the determining genes working differently in the two sexes.

II

The "Bad" Genes

INHERITED FLAWS. Although improvements in environment and medical science have made human beings healthier and sounder in body than ever before in the world's history, there unfortunately are a great many inborn defects which continue to assert themselves. Some of these affect outward appearance; others affect some inner organ or process. Of greatest concern are the inherited defects or abnormalities which severely handicap the person, or doom him to suffering, or cause premature death. Fortunately, most of the serious ills and defects directly and chiefly produced by heredity are not too prevalent; many of those in which heredity plays an indirect part may often be prevented by early safeguards; and even hereditary ailments which already have asserted themselves may in many cases be eased or cured by prompt and effective treatment. (It is a common mistake to assume that because a condition is hereditary nothing can be done about it.) Another fact on the optimistic side is that many human afflictions which in the past were blamed on bad heredity have now been proved to be mainly or entirely due to bad environment. In every case, then, when individuals or members of a family are concerned about a given disease or defect which they know, believe or suspect is hereditary, it is important that they have the basic facts. These facts, with respect to all except very rare conditions of limited interest, we shall try to present in this and succeeding chapters. (See Index for any given condition.)

WHEN IS A DEFECT "HEREDITARY"? There is much confusion on this point. For instance, even doctors sometimes wrongly use the terms *"congenital," "familial,"* and *"hereditary"* as if they meant the same thing. But this may or may not always be so. Here are the differences:

▶ *"Congenital"* refers to a condition present at birth. This need not mean that it is hereditary. While heredity is responsible for or involved in many congenital abnormalities, perhaps the majority are purely environmental. That is, they are *acquired* by the developing baby at some stage before birth, through various unfortunate factors in the mother's womb, such as improper nourishment, lack of certain needed substances, hormonal upsets or prenatal accidents. Also, if there are disease germs in the mother, these may affect the baby and cause it to be born with a congenital disease. *Congenital syphilis* is one example of a disease which can be present at birth and not be "hereditary." Although it was long thought that syphilis could be inherited (the theme of Ibsen's famous drama, *Ghosts*), we know now that neither this nor any other germ disease can be passed along through a parent's genes or chromosomes. The only way any germ disease can appear in a newborn baby is through infection from the mother. (Sometimes a mother can carry the syphilis germs received from the father, without having contracted the disease herself.) *Tuberculosis* is another disease which can appear in a newborn baby through infection by the mother.

▶ *"Familial"* conditions. The mere fact that a disease or defect is repeated in parents and children, or has run in a family for several generations, is again no proof that it is hereditary. Very often the condition is due solely to such environmental factors as dietary deficiencies, bad living or working habits, lack of hygiene or proper medical care, infections, diseases or other harmful influences. It may be only these same influences running in a family which produce the same given diseases or defects. If the environments are changed, such "familial" conditions will disappear. But again, as with congenital diseases, a great many familial conditions *are* hereditary, wholly or in some degree.

▶ *Hereditary conditions.* A condition is called "hereditary" *only if it is produced by a defective gene or genes carried in the chromosomes* received from the father and/or mother. Defective genes may work in a wide variety of ways, and at different stages of life. Some hereditary conditions are also *congenital*, but a great many others are not, since they may not appear un-

til late in childhood, or maturity, or old age. Similarly, hereditary conditions are *familial* only when the genes producing
them are fairly simple and direct in their workings, causing a
given condition to reappear in members of a family for successive generations. However, hereditary conditions are often *not*
familial. This may be true of rare recessive conditions, the two
required genes for which may be brought together by a husband
and wife in neither of whose families the disease or defect had
previously appeared. In other conditions complex gene-workings,
and perhaps special environmental factors as well, may keep an
hereditary condition from cropping out except in occasional instances. And sometimes a defective gene may have suddenly
arisen through a change (mutation), in the mother's egg or father's sperm, so that there would have been no family history of
the condition. (*Mutations:* See Chaps. 3, 25.)

▶ *"Non-hereditary" and "hereditary" distinctions.* The greatest
importance lies in this fact: If a condition is non-hereditary, it
offers no threat at all to the children, or relatives of an afflicted
person, unless it is a contagious disease, and even then only if
transmitted by direct personal contact; but once such a disease
is cured, all threats to others cease. But if a condition is *hereditary*, the threat of transmission is always there, no matter
whether the person carrying the genes for it is himself afflicted,
or was afflicted and had been cured. In short, all non-hereditary
conditions could be wiped out completely and quickly by changing the conditions causing them. But hereditary conditions will
continue as long as the genes producing them are passed along.

HOW "BAD" GENES WORK. "Bad" genes are in many ways
like individuals who misbehave, or don't do their jobs properly,
or create serious difficulties for others. Some bad genes may be
recklessly overactive, producing too many fingers or toes, or too
much of some chemical in the body. Other genes may be shiftless and underactive, not completing the job to which they're
assigned and leaving serious flaws in some vital part of the body
or its functioning. Still other genes work properly only up to a
certain stage of life, and then become shiftless, irresponsible or
worse. Again, many "bad" genes produce only a single, distinctive defect, without impairing anything else in the body's work-

ings. But other "bad" genes, if they are in a key position, particularly at the beginning of life, may start off a chain of defective processes, creating many defects. Such multiple defects which arise from the workings of a single gene are called "*syndromes*." Finally, as with human workers, some "bad" genes go wrong only if in the company of certain other genes, or only in certain environments. Examples of all of these types of genes will be found among the specific conditions to be discussed in the following chapters. (See also illustration, p. 15.)

▶ *"Predispositions" and "tendencies."* Some persons, because of defective genes, have a special weakness in one part of the body or another—brain, heart, lungs, digestive system, or nervous system. Under average or favorable conditions, these persons may function normally. But if there is some unusual stress, or some adverse factor in the environment (infections, dietary deficiencies, etc.) they may have breakdowns or develop diseases, whereas individuals without the defective genes would escape these ills. In all such cases persons are spoken of as having inherited "predispositions," "tendencies" or "susceptibilities" to given diseases. As will be noted in later chapters, many mental disorders, heart afflictions and other serious ailments may depend for their development on degrees of such inherited predispositions.

▶ *"Penetrance."* Geneticists use this term to describe the force with which a gene works. If it shows its full effects under all circumstances, it is said to have "100 per cent penetrance"; if only in half the cases, "50 per cent penetrance," etc. Thus, a condition caused by a single dominant gene with 100 per cent penetrance may appear without a break in generation after generation of a family. But should a gene be incompletely dominant, with partial penetrance (75 per cent, 50 per cent, 40 per cent or whatever), its effects may be discontinuous, failing to show through in many individuals who inherit it.

▶ *"Incomplete recessives."* Just as many "dominant" genes are not always completely dominant (see above), many, if not most genes for recessive diseases may produce some mild effects even in the single state, when coupled with a dominant gene. The importance of this fact will be discussed in a later section, "Tests for Detecting 'Carriers.'"

▶ *Newly mutated genes.* In extremely rare instances two normal parents may unexpectedly produce a child with a defect which is always known to be caused by a single gene (either a simple dominant, or, in sons only, a sex-linked recessive). When it is clear that neither parent could have inherited the gene from his or her family, it may be assumed that the child's defective gene had arisen through a new mutation in a germ cell of one of the parents. Geneticists now estimate roughly that on the average any given gene mutates about once in 30,000 to 50,000 times; also, that some genes are more unstable than others, and mutate considerably oftener than this average, while some very stable genes mutate much less frequently.

MALES AND FEMALES. There are many important differences in the ways in which hereditary diseases and defects afflict males as compared with females—*usually to the disadvantage of the male.* In some conditions the hereditary action is direct, as when it involves genes in the sex chromosomes. (See "Sex-Linked Inheritance," section following.) In other conditions there are general inborn sex differences, in the body construction, body chemistry, organs and functions, which produce differences in the susceptibility or resistance of males and females to given diseases. In still other conditions the environments of males and females (their jobs, activities or habits) may be mainly responsible for the different ways or degrees in which they are afflicted; but even here one must not forget that inborn sex factors may have much to do with directing lives of males and females into different environmental channels. Altogether, it is now recognized that in almost every important disease—mental, organic, functional, infectious—the sex of the individual plays a role in its development and severity. And most amazing, it is becoming increasingly clear that *males, not females, are the weaker sex* biologically. For, as a group, males are more often born defective, are more likely to suffer from hereditary ailments, are inherently more susceptible to most major diseases, and when afflicted are more likely to succumb.

Females are inherently at a disadvantage in only a few categories—afflictions linked with childbearing and their sex organs; cancers restricted to their sex; gallstones; and diabetes, goiter and certain other glandular diseases.

▶ *Prenatal and childhood sex differences.* The fact that inborn, and not environmental factors, are mainly responsible for the greater biological weakness of males is clearly shown by the situation before birth. Among unborn babies the males who die off are markedly more numerous than the females, ranging from perhaps twice as many in the first months after conception, to about 30 per cent more in the later months. Among defective and abnormal babies, miscarried or born, the proportion of males is again very much higher. And in infancy and early childhood— before environments or "conditioning" differ—males continue to die off, become diseased or develop defects, at a higher rate than females. The same is true among many lower animals, from insects to higher mammals. There seems little doubt, then, that females are endowed with many genetic advantages over males.

▶ *Environmental changes.* The reason the inborn advantages of human females were not so apparent in the past was that they were so often canceled out by the strains and mortality tolls of unlimited childbearing. Another reason was (and still is in many backward countries) that very poor environments give the minor inherent female advantages much less chance to assert themselves. But today, as environments have steadily improved, and the special hazards of women have been greatly reduced—much more so than have the special hazards of men— all of women's biological advantages are being manifested to an increasing extent. (See also Chap. 18.)

SEX-LINKED INHERITANCE. Hereditary conditions are called "sex-linked" when the genes responsible are in the sex chromosomes—chiefly the large "X," and in rarer cases, the small "Y." Since females carry two Xs, but no Y, and males carry only one X, coupled with a Y (Chap. 4), defective sex-linked genes work differently in the two sexes, with the males much more often affected. The reason is mainly that if a female receives an X chromosome with a defective gene of the *recessive* type, her other X chromosome usually has a normal matching gene to

Sex-Linked Inheritance

If a defective gene is in the "X" chromosome (as in color blindness)

FEMALE (Carrier) X X

Bad
gene

Normal
gene

With two Xs, a female carrier usually has a normal "X" gene to block the bad one, and is herself normal.

X **MALE (Afflicted)**

Bad
gene →

Y

With only one X, male has no normal gene to block the bad one, and develops the defect.

WOMAN CARRIER'S SONS:

One in two gets mother's bad "X" gene, and has the defect.

One in two gets mother's normal "X" and is not defective.

AFFLICTED MAN'S SONS:

Normal "X"
← gene from
father

← Father's "Y"

No son gets father's X, so every son is free of the defect, and cannot pass on the bad gene.

WOMAN CARRIER'S DAUGHTERS:

One in two gets mother's bad X, and is a carrier like mother.

One in two gets the normal X, and cannot pass on defect.

AFFLICTED MAN'S DAUGHTERS:

Every daughter gets the father's bad X, and is a carrier (like woman at top left of page).

AFFLICTED FEMALE

Only when a female gets an X with a bad gene from both parents will she develop the defect.

Every one of her sons will have this same defect. Every daughter will be a carrier of the gene.

block the effects of the bad gene. Only in infrequent cases do both X chromosomes of a female carry the same defective recessive gene. However, if a male's single X chromosome has a bad gene, this gene alone usually produces a defect in him, for in very few cases does his small Y chromosome carry a matching normal gene. Thus, a great many conditions, of which the best known are *color blindness* and *hemophilia,* are inherited far more often by males than females. In addition, males exclusively are afflicted by the few rare conditions produced by genes on the small Y chromosome. As for females, they run added risks only in the limited instances where defective genes in the X chromosome are *dominant.*

▶ *Transmission of sex-linked defects.* In all conditions where the defective gene is in the X chromosome, transmission to a male can obviously be only through his mother, from whom he receives his single X. Thus, if one of the mother's two Xs is defective, and one normal, the son has an even chance either of inheriting the given defect or escaping it. Should both the mother's Xs carry the same defective recessive gene (which means that she herself would show the affliction) no son could escape inheriting the defect. An afflicted male, in turn, cannot transmit a recessive X-gene condition to his son, who receives only his father's Y chromosome. As for a daughter, while she is certain to get any defective gene carried in the single X chromosome she receives from her father, it will usually cause no damage unless she receives a matching X-chromosome gene from her mother. (See preceding paragraph.) In the great majority of cases, therefore, sex-linked recessive defects skip a generation, passing from affected fathers through unaffected daughters to affected grandsons.

▶ *Dominant "X-chromosome" genes.* A small number of defective genes in the X chromosome are of the dominant type. In these cases an afflicted father will transmit the genes and the resulting condition to *each of his daughters,* but to none of his sons. If a mother is afflicted, there is the same fifty-fifty risk for her sons and daughters alike.

FORECASTING DISEASE INHERITANCE. Doctors are now recognizing that knowledge of hereditary diseases or defects in a patient, or in members of his or her family, may prove important in various ways. This is why they ask details about family histories. Often the information is highly useful in diagnosing early symptoms and taking preventive measures. Where a hereditary condition has already made serious progress in a patient, examination of close blood relatives, particularly younger ones, may often reveal similar hereditary threats, which can be staved off through prompt treatment. Apart from this the facts about disease inheritance may have great importance to parents or prospective parents who know, or suspect, they carry genes for one condition or another, and can weigh the dangers to their children.

Tests for detecting "carriers." What may prove to be among the most important findings of medical genetics is that persons who are themselves not afflicted (or not yet afflicted) by various hereditary diseases, but are carrying genes for them, may be identified by certain special characteristics in their blood, or eyes, or body chemistry, etc. This applies particularly to individuals carrying a single gene for conditions whose serious effects are produced by a pair of the genes. The most striking examples to date are the carriers of single *semi-dominant* genes for either *"sickle-cell" anemia or "Mediterranean" anemia,* who show easily detectable symptoms in their blood. (See Chap. 15.) Also, as previously noted under "Incomplete recessives," many recessive genes in the single state, even when coupled with normal dominant genes, may nevertheless show some effects. Thus, there is limited evidence that tests may identify unafflicted carriers of genes for diabetes, pernicious anemia, schizophrenia, epilepsy and other diseases, and women carriers of single genes for color blindness, hemophilia and other sex-linked conditions. Tests are also being developed to identify younger adults who carry genes for and may ultimately develop Huntington's chorea, hereditary ataxia and several other conditions with late onset. There is hope of eventually greatly extending the identification both of the now unknown carriers of defective genes, and of persons who themselves have inherited a susceptibility to given diseases. (Problems of prospective parents who are carriers of bad genes will be discussed in Chapters 29, 30.)

METHODS OF INHERITANCE. In the case of any given hereditary condition, an absolute essential is that the doctor and the afflicted person (or one who fears transmitting the gene for it) should know the precise mechanism of its inheritance wherever established. Thus, throughout our disease and defect chapters, the known or suspected gene-workings for every condition will be given. In order to save space, abbreviations will often be used. A guide to the meaning of these abbreviations, and the nature of each type of gene, follows immediately. Those desiring a general knowledge of all disease and defect inheritance should study this guide and try to retain the basic facts. Those interested mainly in a few conditions may refer back to this guide as the need for specific information arises.

Guide to Defective Genes
(Meaning of abbreviations used in later chapters)

DOM.

Simple-dominant defect. A single gene will produce the condition. If only one parent is afflicted, there is a fifty-fifty chance any child will also be afflicted. If both parents have the condition, there is a three-in-four threat to any child. (Examples: Huntington's chorea; inner-ear deafness; drooping eyelids.)

DOM.-Q.

Dominant-qualified. (Or "irregularly dominant.") A gene that is often dominant, but whose workings cannot be clearly predicted, because it may be influenced by other genes and/or by environmental factors. Sometimes persons inheriting the gene escape its effects, and sometimes the same gene produces different effects in members of a family. (Examples: skeletal defects; defective hair; "Patch baldness.")

SEMI-DOM.

Semi-dominant. A gene which singly produces only a partial and mild effect, but doubly—one gene from each parent—produces a serious effect. (Examples: "sickle-cell" and "Mediterranean" anemias.)

Guide to Defective Genes (continued)

REC.

Simple-recessive. Two of the same genes, one from each parent, are needed to produce this condition. If both parents are afflicted, every child will be. If neither parent is afflicted, but each is carrying a hidden gene for the condition, there is a one-in-four chance the child will develop it. If only one parent is afflicted, and the other does not carry the gene for the condition, no child will develop the affliction. (Examples: diabetes; amaurotic idiocy; albinism; Friedreich's ataxia.)

REC.-Q.

Recessive-qualified. The pair of recessives which cause this condition do not always show their effects, or the effects may vary, because environmental factors, or some other genes, may be involved. The threats to a child of afflicted parents, or carriers of the genes, are usually less than with simple-dominant conditions. (Examples: rheumatic fever; Laurence-Moon syndrome.)

REC. +

Recessive-plus. Two of the same recessive genes *plus* some other genes are required to produce this condition. Inheritance is less certain than in the case of simple recessives. (Examples: schizophrenia; "Lilliputian" [midget] dwarfism.)

SEX-L.REC.

Sex-linked recessive. A condition caused by a gene in the X chromosome, whose effects are linked with the sex of the individual. (See this chapter, "Males and Females.") Only one such gene will produce its effect in a male, but two genes are needed to produce the same effect in a female. If a father has the condition (examples: color blindness, hemophilia), no son will inherit it, and no daughter will have the condition unless the mother also carries a hidden gene for it; but otherwise every daughter of an afflicted man will be a carrier of the gene and can transmit the condition to one in two sons, on the average. If a mother is herself afflicted with the condition, each of her sons will be afflicted, and each daughter will be a carrier of the gene.

. . . . . .

Cautions:

▶ The non-medical reader should not try to draw precise conclusions about the hereditary threats of any condition without having had competent medical opinion beforehand, so that he will be sure the condition is the one referred to in the text, and is inherited in the way stated.

▶ In many cases the same or similar conditions can be produced either by heredity or by environmental factors (as with various types of deafness, blindness, muscular ailments, etc.). The doctor should study the family history, and if necessary, check medical literature, and/or consult with a medical geneticist, to make sure the condition in question is or is not of the hereditary type.

▶ The *time of onset* is important in many conditions which appear at different stages of life: At birth, in childhood or maturity, or not until middle age or old age. (Example: *chronic simple glaucoma.* Chap. 14.) Where the same condition appears in some families only at one stage of life, in other families at another stage, different genes working in different ways may be involved. Thus, in checking on some variable-onset condition, not only the precise nature of the condition, but the approximate age of the afflicted members of a family, must be known.

12

Inheritance in Major
Organic Diseases

HEART AND BLOOD-VESSEL DISORDERS. These now account for more than half of the deaths in the United States annually. Chief killers among them are high blood pressure (*hypertension*); hardening and thickening of the arteries (*arteriosclerosis*); and rheumatic heart disease (or rheumatic fever). Medical authorities believe that hereditary factors are involved in all of these conditions by way of some degree of predisposition. This means that where any one of these conditions runs in a family, an individual member may have an above-average risk of developing it. The threat is considerably greater as a rule for males, whose death rate from heart and arterial diseases is much higher than that of females. The difference is no longer believed entirely due to the greater strain under which men live and work, or to other conditions to which they are exposed. Various studies indicate that inborn male weaknesses are also involved. (See Chap. 11, "Males and Females.")

▶ *Hypertension* (high blood pressure). This may result from other diseases, or may also lead to other diseases, such as enlarged heart and heart failure, coronary artery disease with blood clots, kidney disease, apoplectic stroke or brain hemorrhage. It is very probable that a predisposition to hypertension is hereditary, although environmental factors are also very important in bringing it on. Some authorities claim a single *dominant* gene may cause susceptibility to the condition in some families, but this has not yet been proved. In any event, where there is a history of hypertension in one's family, a medical checkup is urged to reveal possible threats.

▶ *Arteriosclerosis.* This disease involves thickening and hardening of the arteries, with impairment of blood circulation, leading to heart pains (*angina pectoris*) or damage to the heart muscle (*coronary thrombosis*), and strokes or brain damage. No clear evidence of heredity, but suspicion of it is greatest in cases of *atherosclerosis,* where there are fatty deposits in the arteries caused by improper metabolism of the fatty element cholesterol. Arteriosclerosis is common in persons with gout, which may be hereditary. (Chap. 14.)

▶ *Low blood pressure.* Only in one of the rare types (see your doctor) is this condition inherited, possibly through a dominant gene.

▶ *Varicose veins.* The principal causes and factors are probably in most cases environmental, the condition being most common among persons whose work requires continued standing, and among women after childbirth. In some families, however, a tendency to varicose veins may be inherited, perhaps through an irregularly dominant gene. In such cases if a parent has the condition, the chance is still less than even for any child to be afflicted with it.

Rheumatic fever (or childhood rheumatism). This severe, menacing condition, which afflicts about one in fifty children, is known to run in families by way of a *susceptibility,* probably produced by a single pair of recessive genes (one of which must be received from each parent). The disease apparently develops only under certain conditions still not clearly identified, although it is believed that if the tendency is there, the condition will result from repeated streptococcal infections of the nose and throat. Poor diet and bad, overcrowded living conditions seem to increase the chance of this disease's appearing; nevertheless, it also on occasions strikes children in the most favored groups. Wherever rheumatic fever has previously appeared in a family, it is urgently advised that all younger members be examined for possible symptoms. Prompt antibiotic treatments may overcome the worst threats.

CANCER. There is no proof as yet that heredity is directly responsible for any of the common cancers, although some rare forms of cancer are definitely inherited. Many authorities believe, however, that different individuals are born with varied degrees of susceptibility to given types of common cancer, and that such degrees of susceptibility or predisposition do run in families. The evidence to date shows only that: 1) The incidence of cancer of the breast, or lungs, or uterus, or other parts of the body, is considerably above average in some families, and where a particular type of cancer has appeared previously in a person's close relatives, he or she has a greater than average risk of developing the same condition. 2) Among identical twins, if one has cancer, the other is much more likely to develop cancer of the same type, and sooner, than is the case with fraternal twins. 3) "Cancer-susceptible" strains have been found in lower animals, and it has been possible to breed strains of mice and other experimental animals which will develop given types of cancer according to regular rules of inheritance. However, it has also been shown that cancers can be produced artificially by radiation, chemicals and hundreds of different irritants; that the cancer incidence in human beings is greatly affected by various conditions that are in no wise hereditary; and that even if there are hereditary predispositions, cancer can often be prevented from developing, or if it develops can be cured in a growing proportion of cases.

▶ *Cancer inheritance theories.* Cancer is known to develop when a group of cells in any part of the body "go haywire," or begin to behave abnormally, producing malignant growths. As these cancerous cells multiply, they starve out and destroy surrounding tissues and vital organs, and then may break loose and range like outlaws through the blood stream, creating general havoc. In this process heredity may play a part, theoretically, by way of certain defective genes which could work to 1) derange the cell activities at a given stage of life, particularly during the older ages when body tissues weaken; 2) produce unusual chemical substances or hormones which might irritate cells into becoming cancerous; 3) construct some cells so improperly that it would be easy for cancer to develop under various irritating influences; 4) make the cells unusually susceptible to certain viruses or other cancer-producing agencies. Through any of these theoretical situations, particular combinations of defective genes in given families could cause particular types of cancer to appear with much more than average frequency. But the reader is cautioned not to draw conclusions about hereditary cancer threats in his own case until his doctor has confirmed the facts. For one thing, different types of cancer need not be related. Moreover, the same type of cancer may run in a family only because the members for successive generations were exposed to the same cancer-inducing influences, as in the case of miners, quarry workers, pottery makers, etc., who are in constant contact with irritating dust and substances.

▶ *Sex differences.* The many important differences in the incidence and nature of cancers in the two sexes arise mainly from differences in the sex organs and breasts, but differences in the body functioning, work and external environments also are involved. Females naturally run the special risk of developing cancers of the womb, cervix, ovaries and breasts, while males have a considerably smaller cancer risk associated with their prostate glands and testes. On the other hand, in the non-sexual cancers of the skin, lips, mouth, tongue, throat, lungs, stomach, etc., the male death rate is very much higher. Whether this is entirely due to the greater exposure of males to cancer-inducing conditions and irritants is doubtful. Recent findings are that hormones play a part in the development, and also the treatment of cancer, which suggests that the important hormonal differences between males and females, arising to begin with through the sex chromosomes, may also be involved in the different ways cancers occur and progress in the two sexes.

Breast cancer. Despite conflicting reports and theories, there is enough suspicion of hereditary influence in breast cancer so that if several women in a family have been or are afflicted by it, the daughters or sisters should have frequent periodic examinations in their mature years, and prompt treatment if there are any questionable symptoms. However, the appearance of breast cancer in several successive generations—grandmother, mother, daughter—need not of itself prove inheritance, first because the condition is so common that it might be merely coincidence; second, because the breast cancers in different members might be of different and unrelated types, which had started out at different locations.

▶ *Father's influence in breast cancer:* It should be kept in mind that if there are any genes predisposing to breast cancer, such genes could be just as easily transmitted through a father to a daughter as through mother to daughter. In other words, if breast cancer has appeared in a succession of women on the father's side (his mother, sisters, etc.), his daughters must be alerted to the possibility of symptoms in themselves.

▶ *The "milk factor":* The theory that susceptibility to breast cancer can be passed along through the mother's milk, perhaps by way of a virus or other influence, remains doubtful so far as human beings are concerned, although it has been shown to apply in laboratory mice.

Uterine cancer. Environmental factors, possibly certain irritants, appear to be mostly responsible for cancer of the uterus (or cervix), but recent evidence indicates that hereditary factors may also be involved to some degree. These factors are apparently not related to those producing cancers in other locations (which means that the threat of uterine cancer is no greater or less if cancers of the breast or other parts had previously appeared in close relatives).

Leukemia. Although formerly classified as a "blood" disease, leukemia is today viewed by most medical authorities as a type of cancer of the blood-forming organs, revealing itself through abnormal white cells in the blood stream. The most acute type of leukemia usually appears in childhood without apparent cause. There is some suspicion of hereditary susceptibility, but definite evidence so far applies only to experimental animals. What is clear is that leukemia can be induced through radiation, and doctors and technicians who are exposed to X-rays without adequate precautions have an abnormally high incidence of the disease. In view of this, an enormous threat is posed by the atomic bomb, the explosions of which in Japan resulted in many leukemia cases. Hydrogen-bomb explosions are even more menacing in this respect.

Hodgkin's disease. A rare type of severe, usually fatal anemia, due to a lymph-gland disorder and classified as a cancerous disease. Heredity has sometimes been suspected, but is doubtful.

Intestinal cancer. Heredity may play a considerable part. The strongest evidence is in the case of *multiple polyps of the colon* (smooth growths) which occur in early adult life and in some families are inherited through a *dominant* gene. Despite doubt on this point, it is urgently advised that wherever one person in a family has developed intestinal cancer, the younger members should be immediately examined for possible symptoms.

Stomach cancer. Heredity may possibly be a factor, since the risk of developing stomach cancer for children or siblings of an afflicted person is more than twice the general average. But unfavorable diet does much to bring on the condition.

Lung cancer. There is no evidence of any hereditary predisposition, but the environmental influence is clearly shown by the marked increase in lung cancer in recent decades. Whether this has been due to more cigarette smoking, as some authorities claim, or mainly to other recent irritating influences (such as industrial smoke and dust), is still being debated.

Skin cancers. There is little evidence that any of the common types are hereditary, the principal causes being clearly environmental. However, a person's inherited skin pigmentation may have something to do with the chances of developing skin or lip cancer under exposure to the sun. Thus, fair-skinned persons moving to the tropics run a much higher chance of developing skin cancer than do the dark-skinned natives; and in World War II, among GIs who developed lip cancer while serving in hot climates, those with fair skins were proportionally much more numerous.

▶ *Rare skin cancers.* There are a number of rare types which are definitely hereditary. These, which should not be confused with common skin cancers, include: 1) *Malignant freckles (xeroderma pigmentosum)*, induced by exposure to the sun if the inherited tendency is present. It appears in childhood and is usually fatal. *Recessive.* 2) *Epiloia* ("butterfly rash"), with tumors of the skin and brain, and possibly idiocy, epilepsy or mental derangement. *Partly dominant.* 3) *Coffee-colored spots* (*neurofibromatosis*), associated with numerous dark growths under the skin and also on nerves and in brain. *Dominant.* (Since the two foregoing conditions tend to be dominant, and may be fatal before the individual is old enough to reproduce, many of the genes are believed to arise partly through mutation. Thus, an afflicted child may appear in a family where the condition has never before occurred.)

Rare eye cancers: Two conditions, *glioma retina (retinoblastoma)* and *retinal angioma,* are discussed under "Eye Defects," Chapter 14.

DIABETES. In most cases this disease ("sugar sickness") is mainly the result of a predisposition inherited through *recessive* genes. This means that the inheritance must come through *both* parents, one gene from each. (Some geneticists claim that in certain instances the disease can be produced by a *dominant* gene, passed on by only one parent, but this remains doubtful.) The actual cause of the disease is failure of the pancreas to secrete enough insulin to properly convert the sugar in the body processes, leading to excess sugar in the system which may have serious results unless preventive measures are taken. Unfavorable fatty diets, obesity, overeating, nervous strains, infections and the effects of certain other diseases may serve to bring on diabetes or worsen it; but there is no definite evidence that the disease will develop without some inherited tendency. Especially significant is the fact that many hundreds of children each year in the United States develop diabetes, in most cases despite good diets and wholesome conditions, leading to the conclusion that they are victims of diabetic heredity. Additional evidence: 1) One in four diabetics has diabetic relatives, a far higher than average incidence. 2) Twin studies show that in identical twins, if one has diabetes, so has the other in almost every case. 3) Diabetes has been shown to be inherited in some strains of mice, independently of any environmental influences.

▶ *Sex differences:* Diabetes is one of the few major diseases which afflicts women more than men. Reasons: Women's generally greater susceptibility to glandular diseases; childbearing effects; the longer life span of women, bringing more of them into the "diabetic" ages.

Diabetes insipidus. This condition, often inherited through a simple *dominant* gene (but otherwise due to non-hereditary factors), has no actual relationship to true diabetes. The only similarities in symptoms are an abnormal thirst and frequent urination, but without abnormal production of sugar, or any danger of the condition's developing into common diabetes. Some inherited cases are sex-linked.

▶ *Sugar urine* (*renal glycosuria*). While involving excess sugar in the urine, it has none of the harmful effects of diabetes. Some types *dominant* in inheritance, some *recessive*.

TUBERCULOSIS. The only possible role that heredity can play in this disease is perhaps to make some persons more susceptible to the tuberculosis germs, and others more resistant. Studies among twins in families where tuberculosis has appeared, and with experimental animals, indicate that the chances of developing or resisting tuberculosis may be influenced by inheritance. However, any inherited "resistance" or "susceptibilty" factors are definitely very complex, and are greatly overshadowed by the environmental influences. This is clearly shown by the enormous drop of about 95 per cent in the tuberculosis death rate in the United States during the past fifty years as health, living conditions and medical care have greatly improved. At the same time, the tuberculosis rate remains quite high wherever environments continue to be unfavorable, as in slum areas, and in various foreign countries. Thus, while persons in whose families tuberculosis has appeared should be especially on guard against possible symptoms, the danger of the disease's developing will be very small if living conditions, diet and medical care are adequate.

POLIO (*poliomyelitis,* or *infantile paralysis*). Since threats of this disease appear to have been dramatically diminished by the development and use of the Salk and other vaccines, any hereditary aspects may now be of decreased importance. We refer to findings that while polio results from a virus infection, and is therefore primarily environmental, it also appears that degrees of resistance or susceptibility to the disease may be hereditary, perhaps through recessive genes. For one thing it was found that if one of two identical twins contracted polio, the risk of the other's developing the disease was perhaps six times as great as that when the other of a pair of twins was fraternal.

GOITER. The possible part played by heredity in this disease remains doubtful because development of the common, simple form of goiter depends largely on lack of sufficient iodine in the food or drinking water, causing a strain on and swelling of the thyroid gland. However, even under the same conditions there is evidence that members of some families are much more likely than others to develop goiter, leading to the belief that weakness in the thyroid gland may be inherited, possibly through a *dominant-qualified* gene or *recessive* genes, but this is uncertain. Should there be any susceptibility, the females in a family run about four times as great a risk of developing goiter as do the males, since the female system apparently needs more iodine. A special danger is that when a mother has a thyroid deficiency there is an increased chance of her giving birth to a *cretin* (a type of mental defective; see Chapter 17). In any family where goiter has appeared, a first precaution is to see that there is always enough iodine in the diet.

▶ *Exophthalmic goiter (Graves' disease).* While similar to common goiter in a number of ways (though more likely to be fatal) the cause of this condition is in doubt. It most often afflicts young women who are highly nervous and slender, which may either go with the condition or result from it. Possible inheritance, as in common goiter, may be *dominant-qualified* or *recessive,* though not established.

Ulcers (of the stomach and intestines). These afflictions are considered to be principally brought on by nervous strain, but some authorities believe there is a possibility also of inherited predispositions. For one thing, stomach ulcers are now being found in many babies. Further, the very much higher incidence and seriousness of stomach ulcers in men than in women may be linked in some degree with inherent differences in glandular secretions.

Kidney Disease. It is uncertain whether the common type of kidney disease, *nephritis,* which is one of the top causes of death, is directly influenced by heredity. However, a rare type, *polycystic disease* of the kidneys (especially serious to pregnant women), appears to be inherited in some cases through a *dominant* gene.

Appendicitis. The only suggestion that heredity may be involved in this condition is the fact that it has occurred with considerably above average frequency in some families, leading to the theory that in some individuals there may be a special inborn tendency for the appendix to become diseased.

Fibrosis of the pancreas (cystic fibrosis). A serious disease of both the pancreas and lungs, afflicting perhaps one in eight hundred White children, most often fatally. (Much rarer in Negroes, and almost never found in Mongolians.) Inheritance usually *recessive.*

13
Outer Defects and
Abnormalities

STRUCTURAL DEFECTS. Most recognizable of the human defects and abnormalities are of course those which strike our eyes instantly—unusual sizes and shapes of bodies, peculiarities in bodily details, odd skin conditions, etc. Many of these are inherited, in some cases appearing at birth, but often not until much later. But there also are many similar abnormalities which are purely or mostly due to environmental mishaps or deficiencies in prenatal life. Lack of sufficient oxygen or of needed chemical elements for the developing baby may be among the causes. Very often an environmental abnormality is mistakenly thought to be hereditary, and sometimes the reverse is true; or it may be hereditary in one family but environmental in another. A knowledge of the facts is especially important to persons who have had close relatives or children with any one of the conditions to be described.

STATURE ABNORMALITIES. Human nature tends to be so fairly uniform that a difference of a foot or so above or below the average height range is apt to be considered abnormal. As noted in Chapter 10, human beings as groups have never been deliberately bred to produce extremes in size. Even if this were attempted, it is doubtful if we could produce breeds of healthy humans averaging more than about 7 feet 6 inches tall, or smaller than 3 feet 6 inches to 4 feet. At least that is suggested by such degrees of human stature as have so far appeared.

Dwarfs. These are of several types, with heredity working differently to produce each.

▶ *Midgets* ("Lilliputians," or *ateliotic* dwarfs). Classed as such are the doll-like persons with normal proportions who do not reach beyond about 3 feet 7 inches in height. (The smallest

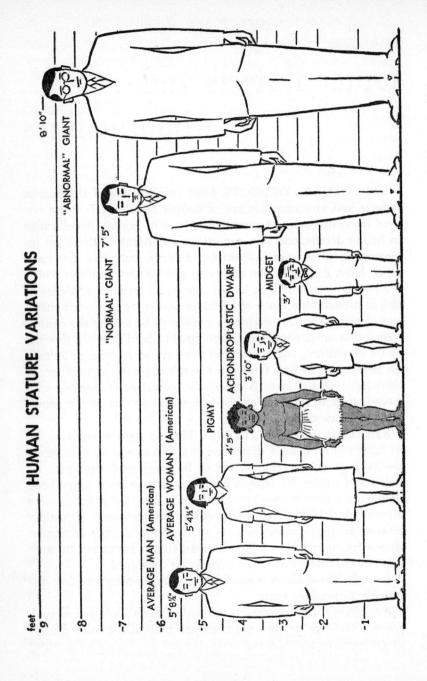

HUMAN STATURE VARIATIONS

feet

-9

-8 — 8'10" "ABNORMAL" GIANT

-7 — "NORMAL" GIANT 7'5"

-6 — AVERAGE MAN (American)

— AVERAGE WOMAN (American)

5'8½"

-5 — 5'4½"

— PIGMY

-4 — 4'5"

— ACHONDROPLASTIC DWARF

-3 — 3'10"

— MIDGET 3'

-2

-1

adult midget on record was 21 inches.) Failure to grow taller results from an inherited deficiency in the pituitary, or "growth" gland, probably due in most cases to *two separate dominant* genes, and in some cases to *simple recessive* genes. Most midgets are born of normal-sized parents (sometimes two or more appearing in a family) because midgets themselves are usually sterile, and if they do have children these tend to be normal in height.

▶ *Achondroplastic dwarfs.* These are persons in whom only the arms and legs are stunted, while the trunk is normal. They also usually have oversized heads and pug noses. Unlike midgets, however, they have average fertility, and often produce children like themselves. In most cases the achondroplastic condition is directly inherited through a single *dominant* gene: If one parent is a dwarf of this type, there is almost an even chance a child of the same type will result, and if both parents are achondroplastic, all or most of their children will be. (In many communities there are whole families of such dwarfs. Among lower animals, dachshunds and bulldogs are achondroplastic, and there are or have been breeds of cows and sheep with the condition.) Occasionally an achondroplastic is born to normal human parents, possibly because of recessive inheritance in some cases; or as the result of a "mutation," or sudden change in one of the parent's genes; or because the gene workings had previously been held back for some reason.

▶ *Pygmies.* These undersized people average about 4 feet 6 inches in height. Whole tribes of them are found in Africa, New Guinea, Malaya and the Philippines. Differing from both midgets and achondroplastics, Pygmies are not abnormal in any way, but are merely undersized because of genes which produce small stature.

Giants. Tallness up to a certain point—seven feet or so—is inherited through "tall-stature" genes, probably working as recessives (as was explained in Chapter 10). But extreme heights of around 8 feet or over are usually due to a glandular abnormality, most often a "runaway" pituitary gland, which gives little evidence of being hereditary. Most of these "pituitary" giants grow weaker as they grow taller, and usually do not survive beyond early maturity. (In the record case, an American youth, Robert Wadlow, reached 8 feet 9½ inches when he died at age twenty-two, in 1940. However, another American, Clifford M. Thompson, who was about 8 feet 5 inches tall, reached the age of 51 and was apparently vigorous when he died in 1955, reportedly from a gallstone and liver complaint unrelated to his size.)

EXTREME FATNESS. Circus "fat ladies" (and men of the same type) are almost always the result of a glandular disorder. (The condition differs in origin from that of ordinary obesity, discussed in Chapter 10.) The record for a fat woman is 772 pounds; for a fat man, 1,000 pounds. Whether heredity plays any part in these extreme conditions is uncertain. Although extremely fat women sometimes have similar daughters, a prenatal glandular influence in the mother may be responsible. (Diabetic women, for instance, may produce abnormally fat children.)

▶ *Myxedema.* A less extreme type of obesity, accompanied by thick, dry skin and sluggishness, resulting from a thyroid deficiency (sometimes with goiter). Heredity in doubt.

HAND AND FEET ABNORMALITIES. These inherited types are of many kinds, almost all due to *dominant* or *dominant-qualified* genes. Thus, the conditions are markedly noticeable in families, since wherever a parent has one of these abnormalities, the odds are that half of the children will have the same abnormality or some variation of it. Often the abnormality also appears in the feet or toes. Most common of these abnormalities (*all usually dominant*) are:

▶ *Stub fingers (brachyphalangy).* Middle joints of fingers missing.

▶ *Extra fingers.* Usually on each hand; often extra toes also.

▶ *"Claw"* or *"split" hand (or foot).* Looking like a lobster claw because of several fingers (or toes) grown together.

▶ *Webbed fingers (and/or toes).* Joined by a flap of skin. Sometimes only slight webbing at base of two fingers.

▶ *"Spider" hand.* Abnormally long, thin fingers (and/or toes).

▶ *Stiff fingers.* Joints fused.

▶ *Other inherited conditions:* Missing fingers or thumbs; double-joints; paddle-shaped thumbs, misshapen toes. (All dominant.)

Clubfoot. In some cases there is a possibility that congenital clubfoot may be inherited, and if so, through *recessive* genes; but in many, if not most cases, prenatal accidents appear to be responsible.

Inherited Hand Abnormalities

STUB FINGERS	"SPIDER" FINGERS	EXTRA FINGERS	SPLIT HAND ("Lobster claw")
Middle joints missing.	Abnormally long and thin.	Usually one, but sometimes two.	Fingers fused.

NOTE: Any one of the above hand conditions may be accompanied by a similar condition in the feet of the individual. All are dominant or partly dominant in inheritance. (See text.)

SKELETAL DEFECTS. All of the following conditions can be hereditary (although sometimes due to environmental factors). Where inherited, the gene in each case is dominant-qualified (Dom.-Q.), not always showing its effects, or sometimes acting only under certain conditions:

▶ *Brittle bones* (*blue sclerotic*) accompanied by bluish eyewhites, deafness, defective teeth.

▶ *Deformed spine* (*Spina Bifida*). Cleft or incompletely constructed spine, with other effects.

▶ *Cobbler's* (*"funnel"*) *chest.*

▶ *Hollow chest* (abnormal type).

▶ *"Tower skull"* (*oxycephaly, acrocephaly*). Several types of high-pointed skull, sometimes with eye or mild mental defects.

▶ *Cranial soft-spot.* Infant soft spot in skull continuing into maturity, with possible other bone defects.

▶ *Courzon's disease* (*craniofacial dysostosis*). Skull and jaw abnormalities.

Congenital hip disease. Dislocation of one or both hips in newborn infants, with girls affected about six times as often as boys. Hereditary influence in some cases, but environmental in others.

TEETH AND MOUTH. Most ordinary teeth defects are undoubtedly due to improper tooth care, diet and faulty eating habits, water elements, etc. But under the same conditions heredity may play a part in giving people "good" or "bad" teeth, well-formed or misshapen teeth. If under different conditions the same teeth defects or peculiarities have appeared in families, heredity may be suspected.

▶ *Missing teeth:* Molars, upper incisors, second bicuspids. Usually Dom., but may also be Rec. or Sex-L. "Fang" mouth, all teeth missing except canines, Sex-L.

▶ *Extra teeth,* frequently with cleft-palate. Dom.-?

▶ *Defective enamel:* Brownish, pitted, transparent, all usually Dom. Reddish enamel (*porphyrinuria*), Rec.

▶ *Malocclusion.* Improper adjustment of upper to lower teeth. Usually appears due to faulty chewing habits, but heredity may also be involved. Dom.-Q.?

Cleft Palate and Harelip. (Together or separate.) Different factors, hereditary and environmental or both, may produce these conditions. If inherited (believed to be in about 20 per cent of the cases), it may be through different types of genes—recessive, sex-linked, or irregularly dominant—often governed by adverse factors in the baby's prenatal environment. As a mother grows older, the risk of having a child with both harelip and cleft palate increases.

SKIN DEFECTS. When concerned about any skin condition in yourself and/or a child, first establish through your doctor that it is not an *acquired* disorder, or due to an internal disease, which is usually the case. Less frequently skin disorders and defects of many kinds are hereditary. Many have no serious effects other than on the person's appearance, but some are dangerous.

Albinism. Rec. or Rec.+. (Previously discussed under Eye, Hair Color.) This is mainly a defect in skin pigmentation, which also affects the other pigmenting processes. The most common type, found among all human beings (Negroes and Mongolians, as well as Whites), is probably inherited through *recessive* genes, but additional genes may also be involved. The highest incidence of albinos (7 per 1,000) is among the San Blas Indians of central Panama. Milder types of albinism: *Albinoidism,* moderate pigment developing in skin and hair, and eyes not affected, Dom.-Q. *Partial albinism* (piebald) with stripes on back, white patches elsewhere, Dom. *White "blaze"* or patch of white hair above center of forehead, usually from birth on, Dom. This latter condition has recently come to be regarded as stylish by some women, and is imitated through bleaching.

Birthmarks. The only ones to be concerned about are the rare types (*malignant freckles,* and *coffee-colored spots,* listed in Chapter 12 under "Skin cancers"), and certain other pre-cancerous birthmarks which are a combination of smooth, hairless, pigmented and not raised, or which suddenly begin to turn black, grow, or bleed. The common types of birthmarks—which are *not harmful*—are those raised, warty and hairy. Often they are purely environmental, but where hereditary, are dominant. (One common type of hereditary birthmark is the *"Nevus of Unna,"* on the nape of the neck.) Wherever in doubt, it is well to check on birthmarks with a doctor.

▶ *Mongolian spot.* A temporary bluish patch near the base of the spine which appears in almost all infants of Mongolian stock (Chinese, Japanese, American Indians, Eskimos, etc.), in many Negro infants, and sometimes in darker-skinned White infants (Italian, Armenian, etc.). Dom. or Rec.+.

Other skin conditions. *Blistering,* abnormal (*epidermolysis bullosa*). Several types: Blisters raised easily from childhood on, Dom.-Q. Severe, birth type, leaving scars, Rec.-Q. Extreme form with bleeding, fatal in infancy, Rec. (partly Sex-L.). *Sunlight blistering,* with scarring (*porphyria*). Mild type, affecting particularly males, Rec.-? Severe form, sometimes fatal, Rec. Another type, due to a metabolic defect in the liver, is Dom.

▶ *Fatty skin growths* (*xanthoma*). On eyelids or elsewhere (*xanthalesma*), Semi-Dom. *Two* of these genes, one received from each parent, will produce the more serious condition, *xanthoma tuberosum,* involving fatty deposits in the internal or-

14651

gans and arteries, the latter a factor in atherosclerosis. (See Chap. 12.)

▶ *Darier's disease.* A "syndrome," which may cause hair-follicle defects, goose flesh, hair loss, stunted stature, sometimes mental deficiency; congenital or in childhood. Dom.-Q or Sex-L.

▶ *Horny skin,* or scaly or "fish" skin (*icthyosis*). Various types: Common, with skin shedding from infancy on, Dom. or Sex-L. *"Elephant"* skin, severe form of cracked skin, causes premature birth and death in infancy, while a milder form may disappear, though may sometimes prove fatal later. Both conditions Rec.

▶ *Psoriasis.* Another "scaly" skin condition, which sometimes runs in families, but if so may be only as a tendency. Has been reported as Dom.-Q. in inheritance, but there may be several genes involved. Possibly also Rec.

▶ *"Rubber" skin (cutis laxa).* Freak elastic skin that can be greatly stretched and snapped back—as much as five or six inches —(as sometimes seen in circus side shows). Dom.-Q.

▶ *Sweat-gland defects.* The complete inability to sweat (with other defects, including missing teeth) is inherited, mostly by males, through a *sex-linked gene.* A milder condition in some families is Dom. An opposite condition, *excessive sweating (hyperhidrosis),* is also Dom.

DEFECTIVE HAIR AND NAILS. There are various rare hereditary types of defective hair: 1) The downy, fine hair of infancy remaining through life. 2) A beady type of hair (*monilethrix*), present at birth and continuing to grow that way. 3) Freakish, excessively long, soft hair on the face and elsewhere, with other effects, appearing in childhood. 4) Defective hair with abnormal nails, appearing at puberty, and found mostly in some French Canadian families. All of the foregoing conditions are either Dom. or Dom.-Q. in inheritance.

▶ *Nails.* Since the nails and hair are fashioned of much the same substances, certain of the hereditary nail abnormalities accompany some of the hair conditions, such as 1) and 4), mentioned above. But some other nail defects and abnormalities are inherited independently. These include absent nails; thick and protruding nails; spotted, bluish-white nails; milky-white nails; thickened nails (with thick skin on palms and soles, also); and thin nails (small and soft, or flat). All the foregoing are usually Dom. or Dom.-Q.; but absent nails may also be Rec.

BALDNESS. The common, widespread type of baldness which comes to about two in five mature and older men, is probably hereditary in the great majority of cases. In these, falling hair and sometimes its almost total loss appear to be unrelated to any disease, state of bodily health or local scalp disorder. Nor is there any truth in the old theory that men become bald and women do not because over the ages men have cut their hair, or taken less care of it than have women. (As previously noted, the habits of ancestors could have no effect on their descendants' inherited traits.) The explanation for the sex differences in baldness, offered by geneticists, is that the baldness tendency results from a special kind of gene, called "sex-influenced" or "sex-limited" because the strength of its effects is governed, or limited, mostly by the sex of the person receiving it. Thus, only *one* of these "baldness" genes can produce baldness in a male, whereas in a female a single gene has virtually no effect, and even two of the genes may produce only a thinning of the hair,

Inherited "Pattern" Baldness

1.

2.

3.

Noticeable loss of hair at forehead, temples and sides. Also, in older men, small bald spot in crown.

Much of hair lost from the forehead to the crown.

Only sparse hair over ears, and in a fringe around the back.

NOTE: Different degrees of baldness, as shown, may run in families. Among women, hair loss rarely goes beyond stage No. 1. (See text.)

or no more than mild baldness. One specific reason seems to be that the male hormones stimulate the "baldness" gene to do its work, whereas the female hormones counteract its effects. Backing up this theory are the findings that baldness rarely, if ever, develops in *eunuchs*—castrated males lacking the normal supply of male hormones—even if they have the inherited baldness genes. But if these same males are given doses of male hormones to make up for their deficiency, baldness develops in those with the inherited tendencies, though not in the others.

▶ *False beliefs.* The above facts should dispose of the old notion that a heavy head of hair in a man indicates virility and potency, while lack of hair suggests the contrary. Actually, once the baldness gene is present, it is the more "feminine" and less virile man (deficient in male hormones) who is apt to retain his hair, whereas it is the more "masculine" man (most abundant in male hormones) who is likely to become bald. But all this applies only to the effects of hormones on the workings of the baldness gene. Otherwise, the fact that a man is or isn't bald proves nothing as to his "manliness."

Inheritance workings. If a young man's father was, or is bald, there is at least an even chance he himself also will be. The threat is increased if there also was or is baldness on his mother's side (her father, brothers, etc.), since a son may have received a "baldness" gene from his mother, even though she herself has shown none of the effects. There are indications that the baldness genes and their effects in some families are stronger than in other families. Thus, degrees of hereditary baldness appear to range from almost total hair loss, beginning to develop in early maturity, to only partial hair loss or thinning in the older ages.

▶ *Race differences.* Baldness genes give evidence of being distributed differently among races and ethnic groups. The most baldness is found among Mediterranean peoples—Greeks, Italians, Turks, Egyptians, etc. Baldness is less common among Negroes than Whites, and least common among Mongolians. (The latter, at the same time, also have less facial and body hair than Whites. See Chap. 9.)

▶ *Non-hereditary baldness.* In a minority of cases, baldness may result from such environmental causes as infectious diseases, glandular and nervous ailments, diabetes, or fevers, which may produce temporary or permanent hair loss. But medical authorities refute the claims of so-called "baldness institutes" that common baldness is caused by dandruff, oiliness of the scalp or simple scalp diseases, and that clearing up these disorders will cure or prevent baldness and restore hair growth. At this writing no cure for ordinary, inherited baldness has been found, and advertising such a cure is forbidden by the United States Federal Trade Commission.

▶ *"Patch baldness."* This is a rare type of premature baldness, unrelated to common baldness, in which a small bald area or patch appears on the scalp, at birth or at puberty, possibly increasing in size and spreading later. The condition may affect girls as well as boys, and is Dom.-Q. in inheritance.

SEX ABNORMALITIES. In infrequent instances the normal processes of sex determination and development (discussed in Chapter 4), can be upset or swerved so as to produce abnormalities of various types. These may include abnormalities 1) in the sex organs; 2) in the secondary sex characteristics (body form, hair growth, breasts, etc.; 3) in the stages of sexual development (greatly speeded up, or much retarded); and 4) in sexual and reproductive functioning. Heredity plays a direct part in only some of these conditions. Most others result from various mishaps, glandular upsets, or diseases in prenatal life or childhood.

▶ *Hermaphroditism.* This refers to an "in-between" sexual development of an individual, with sex glands, organs and sex characteristics of both male and female. The condition may result if the "XY" or "XX" sex-chromosome workings are deranged or impeded prenatally, so that they fail to throw the baby's development fully toward one sex or the other. (Chap. 4.) Only in extremely rare instances (one in many millions) is the individual actually "half" male and "half" female, with both testes and ovaries, and what may pass as a vagina and a penis. (But no case is known of any such human hermaphrodite who was able to function sexually and reproductively as both a male and a female.) Much more common—about one in a thousand persons—are the *pseudo-hermaphrodites,* individuals who are mainly of one sex, with either testes or ovaries, but with outer details of the opposite sex organs sufficiently pronounced so that mistakes may often be made in classifying their sex at birth or later. Whether inherited defects are involved in partial or complete hermaphroditism is uncertain, but there is a possibility that some of the cases which appear to run in families may be due to *recessive* genes.

▶ *"Sex identity" tests.* In many cases where even a medical expert cannot positively determine a person's true sex through ordinary examining methods, it is now possible to establish sex identity by means of a "biopsy test"—a microscopic examination of a bit of the person's cellular tissue. This will reveal whether the cells of the person contain the "XX" (female) or "XY" (male) chromosome combinations. (Chap. 4.) As Professor Murray L. Barr (University of Western Ontario) has shown, this evidence of a person's sex is found in every cell of the body, and even in benign tumors wherever they occur.

▶ *"Sex-changing."* Sensational cases have been reported from time to time of "males transformed into females," or vice versa. In lower animals this is possible, and in some species occurs in the natural state. Thus, the oyster alternates from being a male one season to being a female the next. In poultry, where sex is not as strongly fixed as in humans, hormonal upsets sometimes may cause a hen to develop into a rooster. However, these radical sex reversals have not been found possible in human beings. Most of the reported cases of human sex-changing involved pseudo-hermaphrodites who were operated on to correct abnormalities. The more highly publicized cases of recent years, of physically normal males who claimed to have been turned into females, involved nothing more, according to medical reports, than plastic operations by which the outer male sex organs were removed and female organs simulated.

Genital abnormalities. Among several found in males are the following: *Hypospadias,* a slit or misplaced opening in the underside of the penis. May be hereditary through a partly dominant gene; but may also be non-hereditary. *Cryptorchidism,* failure of the testes to descend into the scrotum. Usually due to non-hereditary factors in prenatal life, but may possibly be hereditary (recessive) in some cases.

Extra nipples (supernumerary breasts). One, two or more additional pairs of nipples and/or breasts sometimes developing in women, and occasionally in men (the extra pairs usually being very small and rudimentary, or merely pigmented areas). Heredity likely in some cases, but factors not clear.

Infantilism. (In females.) Failure of the sex organs and their functioning to fully develop. Heredity suspected in some cases, but gene-workings unknown.

Precocious puberty. A tendency to speeded-up puberty, with its appearance much before average, runs in some families. In extremely abnormal cases (*pubertas praecox*), puberty may begin in girls or boys as early as age three or four. These cases are usually due to glandular upsets or tumors, but where the condition has appeared in successive members of a family for several generations, the possibility of inheritance arises, although the method is in doubt. (A case reported in 1953 was of a Texas boy who at age three had achieved technical puberty and was producing fertile sperms, and whose father, grandfather and great-grandfather, and several other male relatives, had also shown extremely premature sexual development, with no evidence of other abnormalities.)

Sterility. Can be inherited in certain cases through hidden recessive genes carried by normal parents and coming together in a child. In other cases sterility may result from any of various hereditary conditions which affect the sex organs and prevent the production of fertile eggs or sperms. Some types of sterility go with inherited glandular and chemical defects which affect the body as a whole, and often the brain, as in certain forms of idiocy. Other types (rarer) may produce no outward abnormalities, and no detectable symptoms other than lack of fertile sperms in the male; or, in the female, inability to produce fertile eggs or to conceive.

14

Defects in Senses and Body Functions

EYE DEFECTS. Heredity produces or helps to produce hundreds of eye defects, from very mild ones to those causing total blindness. Possibly one fifth of the blindness cases are hereditary, four fifths environmental. More than half of the blindness in young people results from prenatal or later mishaps, such as diseases, infections or dietary deficiencies. But about one eighth of the cases of *congenital* blindness are due to defective genes which fail to construct properly some vital part of the eye mechanism—the iris, retina, eye nerves, etc. In addition, a considerable proportion of the cases of blindness which develop at later stages, in childhood, maturity or old age, are also the result of defective "eye" genes. One important feature of many inherited eye conditions is that they are *sex-linked,* afflicting males much more often than females. (As explained previously in Chapter 11.)

Color blindness. This is the most common of the inherited eye defects and of the conditions which afflict particularly males (about eight times as many as females). Ordinary color blindness is the inability to distinguish the *color* difference between red and green, although, as with red and green traffic lights, the afflicted person might still recognize their difference in shade or intensity. About 4 per cent of White American males have the common form of color blindness, while another 4 per cent suffer from lesser deficiencies in red-green color vision, or other color vision. Among Negro males there is only about half this incidence of color blindness, and among American Indians only about one quarter. Whether any cases of red-green color blindness are due to environmental factors, such as possibly a vitamin A deficiency, is uncertain. (It may be noted that virtually all lower animals, with the exception of monkeys and apes—man's closest animal relatives—are color blind either wholly or to a great extent.) To date no cure for ordinary color blindness is known, although training may increase a color-blind person's ability to distinguish the shade differences between colors.

▶ *Inheritance workings.* These follow the principles of simple sex-linked inheritance (See Chap. 11) in which one color-blind-ness gene produces the defect in males, but two genes are needed to produce the defect in females. Since the color-blindness gene is in the X chromosome, and a male can receive this chromosome only from his mother, it is only by way of their mothers that males can inherit color blindness. For a female to be color blind, both the Xs she receives—the one from her father and the one from her mother—must carry the color-blindness gene, which means that her *father must be color blind* and her mother must be a carrier for the gene. Some women who are carriers, with a single such gene, may show it by a slight defect in red-green color vision if their normal gene does not completely coun-teract the effects of the defective one.

Other visual deficiences.

▶ *Astigmatism* (defective focusing). Its heredity is in doubt but some authorities believe it may frequently be caused by complex genes. Dom.-Q?

▶ *Near-sightedness* (extreme—*high myopia*). May be caused in different families by different types of genes. Rec., Dom., Sex-L.

▶ *Far-sightedness* (extreme and congenital). May be Dom.-Q in inheritance. A serious type, with other eye defects, is Rec.

▶ *Night blindness.* Inability to see in dim light, with possibly other eye defects. Various degrees of this condition and types of inheritance: Dom., Rec., Sex-L.

▶ *Day blindness.* Failing eyesight in bright daylight, and total inability to distinguish colors. Usually Rec.

Eye diseases.

▶ *Cataract.* Most cataracts in children, and many which de-velop in early maturity or middle age, are probably hereditary. (Usually Dom., but with some types Rec. or Sex-L.) It should be clear that some congenital cataracts result from prenatal infections or acquired diseases; and that many cataracts of later life also may be due mainly to diseases and infections, as well as to aging effects. Before concluding that a cataract in any given case is hereditary, the family history must be known. In many families successive cataracts which are very similar in type, severity and age of onset point strongly to the action of dominant-qualified genes.

▶ *Glaucoma.* When occurring in adults and linked with other eye defects, glaucoma may not be hereditary in most cases, but in many families there is considerable evidence that primary glaucoma (not linked to other eye diseases) is inherited possibly through dominant or sex-linked genes. Rarer inherited forms of glaucoma occur in infants (a serious type) through recessive genes, and in children (mostly boys) at puberty, through a sex-linked gene.

▶ *Retinitis pigmentosa.* A very serious hereditary eye disease in which the retina fills with pigment. Different forms and degrees of seriousness (sometimes with deafness, idiocy, etc.), and developing at different stages of life. Inheritance may be Dom., Rec., or Sex-L. Where the gene is sex-linked, women carrying it may sometimes be identified through optical examination.

▶ *Optic atrophy.* Withered optic nerve, causing blindness. Different types, *congenital* (Dom.); *childhood* (Rec.?); *adult* (*Leber's disease*), with blindness only at eye centers, Sex-L., but gene workings not always predictable.

▶ *Cancer of the retina* (*retinoblastoma* or *glioma retinae*). Very rare; congenital or in early childhood, and requiring eye removal to prevent death. Usually Dom., but the gene probably arises in many cases through mutation. *Retinal angioma,* another rare eye tumor, may be hereditary, but how is uncertain.

Eye-structure defects. Among the various hereditary types are corneas that are clouded, or with an opaque ring, or enlarged, or cone-shaped; displaced lenses, sometimes with displaced pupils; irises with a segment missing, or almost closed, or wholly absent. These conditions are most often Dom. in inheritance, but sometimes are Rec. or Sex-L.

▶ *Undersized eyes* (*microphthalmia*). Extremely small eyes, often with other eye defects. (Dom., Rec. or Sex-L.) In a very rare type the eyes are completely absent.

▶ *Cross-eyes* (*strabismus*). This common condition is sometimes hereditary, sometimes not. Where inherited it may be either Rec. or Dom.

▶ *Drooping eyelids* (*ptosis*), in which the eyes always appear to be half-closed. Hereditary, Dom.

▶ *Quivering eyeballs* (*nystagmus*). Appearing at birth, usually with weak eyesight. The common type (Sex-L.) afflicts mostly males. A rarer type, with head twitching, is Dom.

Miscellaneous eye abnormalities.

▶ *Mirror-reading* (and writing). An odd inherited defect which causes persons from childhood on to see in reverse and upside down. Dom.-Q.

Mirror-Reading and Writing
An inherited oddity

Afflicted persons see and write upside down and backwards.
(To see what the boy above has written, hold illustration
before a mirror and look at it with your head turned down.)

▶ *Pink eyes.* Unpigmented eyes, as in albinos, but with no other albino effects. Appears in babies, almost invariably boys. Rare, Sex-L.

▶ *"Dry-eyes"* (*stenosis of lachrymal glands*). Blockage or constriction of the tear glands, so they do not function properly or adequately. Believed Dom. or Sex-L.

Note: For further eye-defect inheritance details, and listing of some rarer eye conditions not discussed here, see *"The New* You and Heredity" (pp. 205-209, 314-316, and references, pp. 594, 595).

HEARING AND EAR DEFECTS. Heredity may be directly or indirectly involved in anywhere from 10 to 45 per cent of the cases of deafness. The exact facts are difficult to establish because diseases and accidents play such a large part in many of the cases, and there is often uncertainty about the causes of deafness in previous members of a family.

Congenital deafness. This may be produced in babies prenatally by various diseases in the mother (German measles, syphilis, etc.) or, following birth, by meningitis, scarlet fever, mumps, etc. But perhaps one third of the cases of congenital deafness in the United States are hereditary, resulting from failure of certain genes to properly control construction of the inner-ear mechanism. If a child is born deaf it is especially serious because inability to hear also interferes greatly with learning to speak. In former times this almost always doomed the congenitally deaf child to be a *mute* as well (hence the common use of the term "deaf-mute"), but today special training helps many deaf children to speak.

▶ *Inheritance.* The manner in which congenital deafness is inherited is still uncertain, but it is believed generally due to *recessive* genes, plus other factors—possibly additional defective genes, or certain adverse influences in prenatal life. This is suggested by the fact that in many cases where both parents were congenitally deaf, children with normal hearing resulted. Generally, however, deaf parents whose condition has not been caused by accident or disease have a much greater than average risk of producing deaf children, especially if they are closely related and are carrying the same genes.

Middle-ear deafness (*otosclerosis*). This is the most common of the serious hearing defects which develop in the more mature years, more often among women than men, and especially after childbirth. Some cases of adult deafness result from injuries and infections, but the hereditary type of middle-ear deafness is caused by a deposit of bony obstruction inside the ear. The genes responsible are usually Dom., but in some instances are Rec. An operation to open the obstruction in the inner ear often greatly improves hearing.

▶ *Inner-ear,* or *nerve deafness,* which comes on usually in middle age, is Dom.

"Word deafness." Hearing normal, but individual cannot interpret sounds and words, due to a brain defect. Appears in early life, most often in boys. Dom.-Q.

Outer-ear defects. Various deformities in the structure of the outer ear, which do not affect hearing, may be inherited. Among them, appearing in babies at birth, are: Absence of one ear; cup-shaped ear (turned over at top); one or both ears "doubled"; a gill-like opening near the ear passage; etc. All *dominant* or partly so.

SPEECH DEFECTS. There is much uncertainty as to hereditary factors in any of the common speech defects, such as stuttering or lisping (when not related to cleft palate or to hereditary nerve and muscle disorders). Many psychologists maintain that stuttering or stammering in a child results mostly from some emotional or psychological disturbance. (Adults, too, may develop speech disorders under stress.) However, certain facts remain puzzling: 1) Under the same conditions only some persons will develop the stuttering habit; 2) stuttering may run in families even when individual members have not been in contact with one another; 3) the incidence of speech defects among males is at least five times that among females, with no proof that this is all due to differences in "emotional" stresses; and 4) among identical twins, if one stutters the other also does almost invariably, which is not so among fraternal twins. Some authorities believe, therefore, that heredity cannot be ruled out as a *predisposing* factor in speech defects. But if there are any genes involved, they have not yet been identified.

▶ *Left-handedness and stuttering.* Despite the wide belief that these are connected, recent evidence indicates that the proportion of "lefties" among stutterers is no higher than the general average. U. S. Army estimates are that 86 per 1,000 selectees—almost one in eleven men—are lefties. (See also discussion of left-handedness in Twins, Chap. 5.)

TASTE AND SMELL DEFECTS. Heredity undoubtedly has something to do with differences in the capacity of individuals to smell and taste substances of all kinds, or of particular kinds, but only limited facts on this point are as yet available. "Taste blindness" with respect to the chemical "PTC" (phenylthiocarbamide) has been found inherited through simple recessive genes. About seven out of ten persons who taste paper impregnated with this chemical say it is "bitter," whereas the rest (those who carry two recessive "non-tasting" genes) detect almost no taste. Possible hereditary differences have also been reported in tasting other chemical substances, which may be related to various foods.

▶ *Smelling defects,* involving the inability to smell some substances, if not most substances, are usually due to nasal diseases, infections or injuries. However, where total inability to smell runs in families, it may be the rare inherited condition of *anosmia,* caused by a dominant gene.

MUSCLE AND NERVE DEFECTS. Doubts exist as to hereditary factors in the more common muscle and nerve disorders, such as multiple sclerosis, but inheritance of some of the special types has been well established. One must be extremely careful, however, not to confuse the hereditary muscular or nerve defects with similar types which are due solely to accidents, injuries or diseases, whether before birth or after. In any case only after a given condition has been properly diagnosed by a competent specialist should the following facts about heredity be considered to apply.

▶ *Ataxias.* Hereditary types include *Friedreich's* in childhood,

(Rec.); *Marie's Cerebellar,* in adults (Dom.-Q.); and hereditary tremor, in childhood (Dom.).

▶ *Paralysis* (referring only to hereditary types): *Spastic paraplegia,* in childhood, chiefly boys, usually Rec.

▶ *Family periodic paralysis,* in adults, Dom. or Rec.

▶ *Wilson's disease.* A peculiar inherited (Rec.) defect in children which is accompanied by facial distortions and jerky hand movements, sometimes also with mental defect.

▶ *Muscular atrophies. Peroneal:* Childhood type, Rec.; young adults, Sex-L. or Dom. *Spinal,* infancy, Rec. *Progressive:* Childhood or pelvic type, Sex-L. or Rec.; adults (shoulder type), Dom.

▶ *Muscular dystrophy, progressive.* Various types, differing in age of onset, symptoms and inheritance: Childhood type, onset age three or four, mostly boys, Sex-L. or Rec. Pre-adolescent type, onset about age eleven, Rec. Young-adult type, onset about age eighteen, Dom. (*Note:* An hereditary strain of mice in which muscular dystrophy appears regularly through recessive genes was reported bred at the Jackson Memorial Laboratory in 1955, and may prove highly useful in studying causes of the disease and its treatment in human beings.)

▶ *Myotonia Dystrophica.* In early life, usually Dom.

▶ *Myotonia congenita* (*Thomsen's disease*). Childhood. Dom.

▶ *Missing muscles.* Various muscles may be left uncompleted or absent through defective genes. Usually Dom.

EPILEPSY. Many authorities now believe that heredity is not involved in the majority of cases of epilepsy, but that in a certain percentage (perhaps 25 per cent or more), heredity does produce some *predisposition* or *tendency*—that is, an inherent weakness in the brain or nervous systems which can lead to epileptic symptoms under unfavorable conditions. These conditions may include various types of accidents and injuries (before birth or after), diseases, metabolic disorders, brain and nerve tumors, etc. The assumption might be, then, that some individuals start off with a nervous system sufficiently unbalanced, because of defective genes, to make them much more likely than average persons to become epileptic under a given environmental "push." Recent findings indicate that persons carrying such genes may be identified through abnormal ("epileptoid") brain patterns. There is also the tentative theory (not yet proved) that one or a pair of these genes may produce the abnormal brain waves without other effects, but that a double dose of the same genes may produce epilepsy or the tendency to it. However, only *one rare* condition—*myoclonus epilepsy* (differing in many ways from the ordinary types)—has so far been proved directly hereditary, through *recessive* genes.

▶ *Heredity evidence.* Various studies indicate that 1) among identical twins, if one is epileptic, the other will also show an abnormal brain-wave pattern and will be epileptic in about 70 per cent of the cases, whereas among fraternal twins both are epileptic only a fourth as often; 2) among close relatives of epileptics the incidence of epilepsy is about five times that in the general population; 3) the abnormal "epileptoid" brain waves seem to run strongly in certain families, and if a child is epileptic, the "epileptoid" brain waves will appear in one parent, if not both.

▶ *Epilepsy and mental defect.* In the large majority of cases there is no relationship between epilepsy and intelligence. About two thirds of the epileptics are average or above average in IQ; about 23 per cent are slightly below average, and only 10 per cent are retarded sufficiently to be placed in institutions. Epileptics most likely to be mentally defective are those whose condition result from brain injuries, and not from any inherited tendencies.

▶ *Incidence.* The best estimates are that incidence of epilepsy in the United States today is well above one half of one per cent, and possibly close to one per cent, so that somewhere between a million and a million and a half persons are affected in some degree.

CHEMICAL DISORDERS. The more serious and common disorders resulting from possible hereditary defects in the body's chemical process have been previously discussed (Chap. 12) or will be dealt with later (blood conditions, mental diseases and defects, etc.). Here we will deal with a few other conditions to which heredity may contribute.

▶ *Gout.* The long-standing suspicion that this has an hereditary basis is borne out by recent findings that a susceptibility to gout results from an excess of uric acid in the blood (*hyperuricemia*) caused by a *dominant* gene. Further, the much higher incidence of the disease among males is explained by the fact that the male chemical makeup is particularly likely to promote the development of gout if the tendency is there, whereas the female chemical environment may help to suppress it. (However, only about 10 per cent of males with hyperuricemia develop gouty arthritis.)

▶ *Urinary disorders.* Various types, identified by unusual amounts of different substances in the urine, and producing different effects, are hereditary: *Porphyrinuria* (with reddish teeth); *alkaptanuria* (darkish urine) sometimes with arthritis; *cystinuria,* occasionally with kidney stones; *pentosuria,* a sugar-assimilation defect. These conditions are all usually *recessive.* (See also, *Blistering, Sunlight,* Chap. 13.)

▶ *Fat-metabolism defects.* One of the more common conditions, *xanthoma,* was discussed under "heart afflictions," (*atherosclerosis,* Chap. 12). Others fairly well known are *Niemann-Pick disease* (liver and spleen enlargement) and *Gaucher's disease,* both afflicting mostly children, with serious consequences. (Rec.-Q.?) Inherited defects of fat metabolism also are involved in *amaurotic idiocy,* and *gargoylism.* (Chap. 17.)

ALLERGIES. Innumerable differences exist among human beings in the way they react to foods and drugs of all kinds, and very often heredity is involved. When the reaction produces unfavorable results, it is called an "allergy." Probably every person is allergic to one or more things, which may be the fur of a particular animal, feathers, dust, or any of hundreds of foods, drinks, drugs and chemical substances. Very often allergies result in or are linked with violent hay fever, asthma, or certain skin diseases or digestive disturbances, which in children may interfere with proper growth and development. Many authorities today believe that what causes an allergy to become acute is usually or often some emotional ("psychosomatic") disturbance in the individual which makes the chemical reactions of the body especially sensitive. However, the fact that individuals tend to be allergic only to *particular* substances, and that such allergies, often of a peculiar nature, tend to run in families, strongly suggests that heredity is also involved as an influence or direct cause, perhaps in three fourths of the cases. There is some evidence that allergy inheritance may be *dominant*. One theory is that there are two kinds of dominant "allergy" genes: If both kinds are inherited, allergic symptoms are likely to appear before puberty (in boys twice as often as girls); with one gene alone, a milder allergy will appear, after puberty. Another and recent theory (Robert L. Tips, 1954) is that susceptibilities to *hay fever,* or *atopic asthma,* or *eczema,* are caused by variations of recessive "hypersensitivity" gene pairs.

▶ *Migraine headache.* This is sometimes viewed as an allergic condition, and is probably *dominant* in inheritance. Women are afflicted by migraine twice as often as men, the condition appearing to be aggravated by female hormones, and the worst attacks coming during menstrual periods.

▶ *Angioneurotic edema.* A rare, very serious allergic affliction in young people (twice as many boys as girls), which may produce sudden swellings in the larynx or vital organs, sometimes causing death. Dom.

15
Blood Types and
Conditions

BLOOD INDIVIDUALITY. As the most vital fluid of the body, blood has been given much careful study. Many important hereditary differences among individuals in their blood elements and blood cells have been found. Some of these blood differences involve abnormalities, deficiencies or diseases with varying consequences, ranging from mild defects to serious and fatal results. Other differences have importance only in certain situations, as in transfusions, when the blood of one individual is mixed with that of another. Discoveries of the blood types and of methods for "typing" persons have eliminated most of the grave dangers which attended transfusions in former times.

Blood-type inheritance. The main blood-type differences among human beings—in the "*A*," "*B*," "*AB*" and "*O*" groups— involve the presence or absence of certain chemicals in the red blood cells. The *A* substance is determined by one *dominant* gene, the *B* substance by another *dominant* gene. In addition there is an *O* gene which determines neither substance, and is *recessive* to the other two genes. Since a person must receive one of these three blood genes from each parent, six paired combinations are possible. *A* blood will result from either an "*AA*" or an "*AO*" gene combination (the *O* gene being recessive). Similarly, *B* blood will result from either a "*BB*" or a "*BO*" combination. But if a person receives an *A* gene from one parent, a *B* gene from the other parent, *AB* blood will result, because neither gene dominates the other and both *A* and *B* substances are produced. Finally, *O* blood will result only if an *O* gene is received from each parent.

▶ "*M-N*" *and other blood types.* In addition to the *A-B-O* blood substances (and the "Rh," to be discussed later), there

119

are a number of less important inherited blood substances. Among them are the *M* and *N* substances, inherited through mutually dominant genes, so that a person getting an *M* gene from one parent, an *N* gene from the other, would be the *M-N* type. Other blood substances recently discovered are the so-called "*S,*" "*Kell,*" "*Duffy*" and "*Lutheran.*" Many of these, especially the *M-N* substances, are of interest so far mainly in disputed paternity cases (Chap. 28) and in racial studies (Chap. 26).

Diseases and blood types. Limited recent evidence suggests that persons of some blood groups may be somewhat more prone to develop certain diseases than are persons of other blood groups. Such associations are claimed between blood-group *O* and duodenal ulcer, and between blood-group *A* and cancer of the stomach, and also, possibly, diabetes in males. Further study of these points is needed before they can be accepted as proved.

TRANSFUSIONS. The most important application of the *A-B-O* blood-type findings is in transfusion, for if a person is infused with blood of a different type from his own, there may be a clumping or disintegration of the introduced blood cells. The greatest danger arises if an *O*-blood person receives blood of any of the other three types; or if an *A* person is given *B* blood, or a *B* person is given *A* blood. An *AB* individual can most safely receive blood of other persons. Contrariwise, *O* blood, lacking *A* and *B* substances, can be transfused with least risk into persons of other blood types. But the term "universal donor," formerly applied to an *O* person, is no longer used, since any *O* donor might also be carrying additional blood substances which could be harmful if transfused into another person who lacks them. (Among these substances is the "Rh factor," to be discussed presently.)

▶ *Family blood-type relationships.* An important fact to keep in mind is that the blood types of two members of a family may differ through inheritance just as their hair color, eye color or other traits may differ. Thus, where these differences occur, there may be precisely the same danger in transfusing a mother's blood into her own child, or the blood of one brother into another, as in transfusing blood from any unrelated person. On the other hand, the blood of an outsider, even of a different race, can be safely transfused into a person with the same blood type.

THE "RH-DISEASE" (*erythroblastosis fetalis*). This now widely known blood affliction of certain newborn babies is produced in prenatal life by hereditary factors working in an indirect way to cause conflict between the baby's blood and the mother's. The disease itself is not inherited, but can develop *only* when the baby's blood carries an inherited chemical substance known as the "Rh factor," and the mother's blood lacks this substance, being of the inherited type known as "Rh-negative." But even then, there is danger to the baby only in a very small percentage of the cases, for reasons which will become clear when we see the sequence of things which must happen:

1. In the course of prenatal development, some of the baby's red blood cells with the "Rh-positive" substances must break through the barriers of the placenta and filter into the mother's circulation.

2. The mother's body must respond by producing "*antibodies,*" or "anti-Rh" counteracting chemicals, to fight off the foreign "Rh-positive" red blood cells.

3. The "Rh" antibodies in turn must pass into the baby in sufficient amounts to cause serious injury to his blood cells. Altogether, the serious results may occur in no more than *one in sixteen* of the *one in twelve* cases where the mother is "Rh negative" and the baby "Rh positive"—or about one in two hundred pregnancies. Particularly with a *first* baby, the mother's blood will probably not yet have developed enough of the "anti-Rh" substances to seriously endanger the child. The major threat comes if the mother's blood has started off with "anti-Rh" substances developed in her through some prior transfusion with "Rh-positive" blood; or, if this is not her first pregnancy, she previously had carried an "Rh-positive" baby (or two or more such babies) with whom she had had a blood-substance exchange. (See illustration, page 123.)

The "Rh" genes. The gene that gives rise to the "Rh-positive" type is *dominant;* the gene for "Rh negative" is *recessive.* Thus, to have "Rh-positive" blood a person need inherit only one "Rh-positive" gene. But to have "Rh-negative" blood a person must receive *two* "Rh-negative" genes, one from each parent. The relative proportion of "positive" and "negative" persons varies with racial groups. Among Whites, about 85 per cent are "Rh positive," 15 per cent "negative." Among American Negroes only 8 per cent are "Rh negative," which means the threat of the "Rh-disease" for their babies is much less than for White babies. Going further, among Chinese, Japanese and other Mongolians, there are virtually no "Rh-negative" individuals, almost all being "positive," so there is no "Rh-disease" threat for Mongolian babies unless their parents carry some White genes.

Predicting "Rh" threats. Knowing the facts regarding "Rh" inheritance, it is now relatively easy to establish in advance whether a given baby of a given couple is threatened by the "Rh disease." There is no threat at all (with rare exceptions) if the mother is "Rh positive." But if she is "Rh negative," the father's blood must immediately be tested. Unless he is among the one in seven (Whites) who are "negative" one must go on the assumption that the baby will be "positive" and that there may be a blood clash with the mother. Thus, the mother must be tested further to see if her blood is already carrying "anti-Rh" substances, either through earlier "Rh-positive" pregnancies or transfusions. If she does carry these "Rh" antibodies, and is already pregnant, the likelihood is that her baby is developing the "Rh-disease." Dangers may then be reduced, if a child is born with gravely impaired blood cells, by an immediate blood-exchange process, with all of the defective blood replaced by healthy new blood. With the various precautions now possible or being developed, there is little danger to a first "Rh-positive" baby of an "Rh-negative" mother, and only slight danger for a second such baby.

▶ *Other child-mother blood conflicts.* Conditions similar to the "Rh disease" may sometimes (though rarely) result even if mother and child are both "Rh-positive" or both "Rh-negative," but have clashing differences in other inherited blood elements. These differences may involve the *A, B,* and *O* blood-type substances, and in some instances, certain special "Rh" elements.

▶ *The "Rh" discoverers.* Credit for the discovery of the "Rh factor" (in 1939), its method of inheritance and its role in blood

How an "RH-Disease" Baby Is Produced

1. CHILD receives from **FATHER** an "Rh-positive" gene, and begins to produce "Rh-positive" blood, shown by symbol ⊕

2. MOTHER'S blood is "Rh-negative," shown by symbol ⊖

3. Some of the **CHILD'S** "Rh-positive" blood substance travels through placenta into **MOTHER**

4. **MOTHER'S** blood begins producing **ANTIBODIES** to attack hostile substance*

5. ANTIBODIES FROM MOTHER ENTER CHILD AND BEGIN DESTROYING ITS BLOOD CELLS

*If "Rh-negative" mother has had previous "Rh-positive" pregnancies, or transfusions with "Rh-positive" blood, antibodies already are present.

(Chart prepared with aid of Dr. Alexander Wiener.)

(From *The New* YOU AND HEREDITY. Copyright, 1950, by Amram Scheinfeld.)

transfusion and the "Rh disease," goes mainly to three Americans, Dr. Alexander Wiener and Dr. Philip Levine, and the late Dr. Karl Landsteiner with whom they began their work. Many other experts have since helped in the researches which have led to the saving of thousands of babies yearly.

See also: *Race differences in blood types,* Chap. 26; *Disputed Parentage Cases,* Chap. 28.

HEMOPHILIA. While comparatively rare, this is the best known of the inherited blood diseases, mainly because of its appearance in European royal families. This in turn helped to draw attention to its inheritance as a *sex-linked* condition, confined almost exclusively to males, and passed along to sons through mothers. As is now clear, hemophilia (which is by no means confined to royalty, but is found in all social levels, nationalities and races) results from a defect in a gene in the X chromosome concerned with blood clotting, or coagulation. (There are about five varieties of hemophilia, each with a deficiency of a particular compound.) Since the male receives only one X, and this from his mother, the defective gene will impair his blood-clotting process. But since a female receives two X chromosomes, her other, normal gene, will insure normal blood clotting. For a woman to receive *two* "hemophilia" genes, it would be necessary for her father to be a hemophiliac and her mother to be a carrier for the "hemophilia" gene—an extremely unlikely situation. One reason is that most male hemophiliacs have usually died in childhood or early maturity, before they reproduced; another probability is that if a girl baby did receive two hemophilia genes, the double dose would bring death before birth or soon thereafter. Nevertheless, a few cases of women presumably with hemophilia are in the medical records. (The disease has recently been discovered in dogs, where it is inherited as in man. This opens the possibility of new experimental studies leading to remedies.)

▶ *"Royal" hemophilia.* The gene for hemophilia appears to have arisen in Queen Victoria, or in her mother, through a *mutation*— the way in which many other hemophilia genes are believed to arise. (Were it not for these new mutations, the hemophilia genes in circulation would eventually be depleted by early deaths of the afflicted males.) Records indicate that Queen Victoria transmitted the gene to four, or possibly five, of nine children, including Leopold, who was a hemophiliac (and perhaps another son, who died in infancy), and three daughters, Victoria, Alice and Beatrice. These last three "carriers" passed the gene on to various of their children and grandchildren. Luckily for the present British royal family, Queen Victoria's heir, Edward VII, did not receive the dreaded gene, so that none of his descendants is threatened by the disease. (Although Prince Philip, husband of Queen Elizabeth II, is also a descendant of Queen Victoria, he, too, is free of the hemophilia gene.)

▶ *Pseudo-hemophilia.* This bleeding condition, much milder than hemophilia, is inherited differently, through a *partly dominant* gene, and afflicts females as well as males.

Agammaglobulinemia. A recently discovered blood deficiency inherited by males, like hemophilia, through a sex-linked recessive gene. The afflicted males lack *serum gamma globulin* and so cannot produce protective antibodies in their blood against various infections and diseases. Formerly they would usually die in childhood but can now be kept alive with antibiotics and gamma globulin.

Bleeding under the skin (telangiectasis). Due to abnormally formed fragile blood vessels. This condition is inherited as a dominant. The most common symptom is frequent nasal bleeding (*epistaxis*), but different from ordinary nose-bleed.

ANEMIAS. Most of the common anemias, which involve deficiencies in the quantity or nature of the blood, result from diseases, infections or malnutrition. However, a number of types are directly due to inherited abnormalities in the blood cells. Two of these widely known conditions, *"Mediterranean"* (*Cooley's*) *anemia,* and "sickle-cell" anemia (unrelated to one another) are of particular interest because each is largely confined to persons of specific racial groups, and because of their unusual method of inheritance. In both of these conditions (as Dr. James V. Neel has shown), *one semi-dominant* gene produces certain mild effects; a double dose—two of the same genes—produces extremely serious effects. Fortunately, the mild effects caused by a single gene make it easy to identify the persons carrying it and to provide ample forewarning of the dangers to prospective children if two such carriers marry.

▶ *"Mediterranean" anemia.* So called because it is found mostly among persons of Mediterranean stock—Greeks, Italians, Armenians, etc. (although it also occurs in Southeast Asia). The dominant gene responsible produces only mild blood abnormalities if inherited from just one parent. But if a child receives two of the genes, one from each parent, there will be very serious effects in the entire system, including skeletal abnormalities, Mongoloid features and disturbances which usually bring death in childhood.

▶ *"Sicklemia"* and *"sickle-cell" anemia.* These conditions, which afflict chiefly Negroes, are also inherited by the *semi-dominant* method. A single gene, from one parent, will cause the mild condition of "sicklemia," in which a small percentage of the red blood cells have a peculiar, twisted "sickle" shape, but with the individual otherwise normal. However, two of the same genes— one from each parent—will cause a high proportion (half or more) of the red blood cells to have the abnormality, and to be so defective that fatal anemia may result. The mild and harmless one-gene condition of sicklemia occurs in close to 10 per cent of the American Negroes (and 15 per cent or more of those in Africa). Not only is this condition harmless, but recent studies indicate that it may help to provide resistance against malaria, and may be one reason why the malaria incidence is much lower among Negroes than Whites in the same environments. The serious double-gene anemia occurs in about one in three hundred Negroes. Here again, as with "Mediterranean" anemia, the incidence of the serious disease can be greatly reduced if persons with the easily recognized one-gene condition avoid marrying similar carriers.

▶ *Pernicious anemia.* A chronic, serious blood disease of maturity, due to a defect in the stomach lining; often running in families, but with the method of inheritance not clear. Possibly recessive or incompletely dominant. Considerably more common among Whites than among Asiatics and Negroes. Children and other close young relatives of a pernicious-anemia sufferer run a much higher than average chance of developing the condition.

Early detection of symptoms may prevent the more serious results.

▶ *Congenital hemolytic anemia (or acholuric family jaundice).* An anemia with abnormal, fragile blood cells. Inherited usually through a dominant-qualified gene which does not always assert itself. In some families the disease takes a less severe form than in others.

▶ *Polycythemia (erythremia).* Excessive production of red blood cells and blood, which appears to be inherited in some families, but in what way not yet established.

Harmless blood-cell abnormalities. Among a number of inherited blood-cell anomalies which have no harmful effects are *oval-shaped,* or elongated red corpuscles, and undeveloped white blood cells (*Pelger's anomaly*). Both are usually dominant.

Leukemia. See under *Cancer,* Chap. 12.

16

Mental Diseases

"INSANITY." Fears of "inheriting insanity" are probably greater than those regarding any other type of affliction, and go back to earliest human history. First it should be clear that "insanity" is now only a popular term, applied to mental diseases without distinguishing one from the other. But actually, as modern psychiatry has shown, there are many types of mental diseases, different in their symptoms and causes. This is especially true with respect to *hereditary* factors or influences. In some conditions—mostly the rarer ones—heredity plays a direct and major role; in others it produces *tendencies* or *susceptibilities,* which will give way to insanity only if there is some strong, adverse environmental push. In any case, in each type of mental disease heredity may work in a different way and in a different degree. Accordingly, wherever persons fear that they or their children are threatened by insanity because it has appeared previously in their family, they must be careful to establish the type of mental disease with which they are concerned, and then note how heredity may be involved. But before taking up the mental diseases separately, a few special points should be made clear:

▶ *Insanity incidence.* Roughly, close to one in every twelve persons in the United States is, or will be at one time or another, afflicted by some mental disease requiring hospitalization. Does this mean that *every* person has an up to one-in-twelve risk of becoming insane? No. For some individuals there may be almost no risk; for others it may be considerably higher than one in twelve—in rare instances up to fifty-fifty. The risk in each case is determined by the nature of the mental disease, the relative influences of heredity and environment, the age at which the condition usually appears, and the individual's own makeup, habits and experiences.

128

▶ *"Are people becoming crazier because of modern pressures?"*
This is hard to answer. Although there are now vastly more people in mental institutions than there formerly were, there are
many reasons for this: Mental cases are diagnosed more quickly
and expertly; the facilities for taking care of the mentally sick
have enormously increased, so many more people can be put in
mental hospitals; lengthening life spans have swelled the numbers of mentally ill old people; and the mental casualties of two
terrible World Wars have added thousands of others. Yet it also
is possible that the complex conditions and pressures of modern
life have made it more likely for mental diseases to develop in
unstable persons. One can only guess about this, since there are
no accurate medical facts from former times with which to make
comparisons. Similarly, one can draw no conclusions about the
incidence of insanity in the United States as compared with
other countries, or among those of one race or ethnic group
compared with another, so long as the facilities for detecting
and caring for the mentally ill differ so greatly. However, in most
advanced countries, such as England, Sweden and Denmark,
the proportion of mentally ill is much the same as in the United
States. Moreover, wherever psychiatrists have investigated, even
among the most isolated primitive peoples living under the simplest conditions, they have found many cases of mental illness,
which again strengthens the belief that the inborn tendencies
are universal.

▶ *"Can environmental factors or emotional stresses alone produce insanity?"* Most authorities are now inclined to believe that
except in very unusual cases, a person will not become insane
unless he starts off with some inborn tendency. No more terrible,
nerve-racking experiences can be imagined than those which
vast numbers of soldiers and civilians underwent during World
War II. Yet only a relatively small proportion became mentally
diseased. Evidence indicates strongly that those who did were
especially *susceptible.* Further, there is considerable evidence
that even *chronic alcoholism, syphilis* or other acquired diseases,
do not ordinarily result in mental derangement unless there is
some predisposition; and that in very old age, while mental fac-
ulties may become weaker, actual insanity (*senile dementia*)

tends to occur only in those persons who previously had some mental instability. Finally, there is no evidence that any one can ever "catch" insanity merely from contact with a mentally diseased person, no matter how close the relationship.

▶ *"How can heredity produce mental disease, or the tendency?"* Since the human brain is a very complex organ, or "mechanism," in whose construction and functioning many genes must take part, abnormalities in any of the "key" genes may upset, derange or unbalance the mental workings at any given stage of life, especially when there is some severely jarring outside influence. Recent studies suggest that these abnormalities may include particular kinds of chemical or hormonal upsets or deficiencies which directly affect the brain cells and disturb or prevent their orderly workings.

▶ *"If a person inherits 'insanity' genes, does this doom him to insanity?"* Not necessarily, and perhaps not at all in many cases. Mental disease need be no different from other diseases, whether inherited or acquired, in the possibilities for prevention and cure. Psychiatrists are making increasing headway in combating threats of mental disease with various means of treatment, among them—most recently—with drugs, such as reserpine and chlorpromazine. This strengthens the theory regarding chemical factors as involved in some of the conditions, and opens the possibility that much more will be done in combating them. Especially important has been the progress in detecting symptoms of mental disease in the early stages, through various behavior clues and tests, and in some cases through abnormal brain-wave patterns. However, laymen are warned not to make judgments for themselves on the basis of any "peculiar" behavior, which may often stem from temporary emotional difficulties rather than any mental disease.

▶ *"How is 'mental disease' different from 'mental defect'?"* There are very important distinctions. "Mental disease" refers solely to a *derangement* of the mind, without regard to the person's intelligence, which may be of any level up to the highest. "Mental defect" refers to a *slow-working* or *inferior* mind, which prevents the person's intelligence from going above certain levels. The two conditions are entirely different in their causes and symptoms. Where in some cases a person is both mentally *diseased* and mentally *defective,* it is mostly coincidence. In this chapter we will deal only with mental diseases; in the next chapter with mental defects.

SCHIZOPHRENIA. This is the most serious of the common mental diseases, because it starts earliest, is hardest to *cure,* and accounts for more than half of the persons in mental institutions. The name of the disease comes from two Greeks words, "*schizo,*" meaning "split," and "*phrenia,*" mind, and is so called because the afflicted persons tend to have a mind or personality "split" between the normal and abnormal. The disease is sometimes also called *dementia praecox* (the "praecox" from the Latin for prematurity) because it often appears before or during adolescence, earlier than other common mental diseases. When one reads about demented little children, or high-school boys or girls with mental breakdowns (sometimes leading to suicide or acts of violence), the disease usually is schizophrenia. It first shows itself as a rule by extreme shyness, timidity, not mixing with others, indifference to outside things, etc., accompanied by hysterical periods and other symptoms. There are various types of schizophrenia each with special characteristics: quarrelsomeness and delusions of persecution (*paranoia*); pleasant stupor (*hebeprenia*); violent tantrums, obstinacy or rigidity (*catatonia*). Milder types may show themselves only by occasional freakish or erratic behavior.

▶ *Hereditary factors.* On the basis of many studies, it is believed that schizophrenia is not likely to develop unless there is an inherited predisposition, probably produced through several defective genes—*a pair of recessives,* and perhaps other genes, or other biological factors. This would mean that a child cannot inherit schizophrenia (or the tendency) *from one parent alone,* but must receive one or more of the "schizophrenia" genes from *each* parent. In the unfortunate cases where couples do have a schizophrenic child, neither parent therefore has the slightest basis for saying, "It's all because of that insane streak running in *your* family." Any such inherited tendency in a child would have had to come equally through *both* parents. However, a bad emotional environment in the home, or exposure of the child to special strains, might cause the schizophrenic tendency to develop into the disease itself, and to that extent one parent might be more to blame than the other.

▶ *Evidence for heredity.* In the general population the average incidence of schizophrenia is about 0.8 per cent, or somewhat under 1 per cent. But wherever close relatives of a person have or had schizophrenia, the threat of developing the disease is very much higher than the average: twenty times the average if a parent was schizophrenic (with the risk rising to an almost two-in-three threat if both parents were so afflicted); fourteen times the average if a brother or sister was schizophrenic; and five times the average if a grandparent, uncle or aunt had the disease. Among twins, if one of an identical pair is schizophrenic, there is a three-to-one or even four-to-one chance the other will also be or become so, whereas in fraternals the disease occurs in both no more often than in two non-twin children of a family. But the fact that among identical twins one can be schizophrenic and the other not, although carrying the same hereditary factors, shows also how important are environmental influences.

Childhood schizophrenia. Adding to the belief in the inheritance of the schizophrenic tendency are the increasing numbers of cases of this disease found in very young children, at age two or earlier. Often the disease appears spontaneously, with no evidence of anything wrong in the child's environment. Some psychiatrists believe that babies who are deprived of love and proper attention are most likely to become schizophrenic, but there is strong doubt as to whether any baby will develop the disease unless an inborn tendency was present. Strongly supporting this assumption are recent (1955) findings by Dr. Franz Kallmann that children with schizophrenia had schizophrenic relatives in almost the same higher-than-average ratios as were given for afflicted mature persons in the preceding paragraph. In any case, if a schizophrenic child appears, it is grossly unfair to blame the parents without full knowledge of the facts.

MANIC-DEPRESSIVE INSANITY. This disease is so called because those afflicted may swing in periodic moods from mania (highly excitable and sometimes hilarious behavior) to extreme depression. As the disease progresses it may lead to violent outbursts. But on the whole, manic-depressive insanity is less serious than schizophrenia because 1) it takes less toll in years, most often appearing later in life, during maturity or in middle or old age (although cases are now also being recognized in young children); and 2) it is curable more often and more easily, many manic-depressives recovering after treatment of six months or so (although a dangerous part of the disease is that sometimes individuals who appear cured may suddenly crack up again and commit criminal acts).

▶ *Hereditary factors.* There is a strong probability that a tendency to manic-depressive insanity is inherited, but differently and independently from schizophrenia. Although not certain, it is believed that the "manic-depressive" genes are *partly dominant,* or *irregularly dominant,* and that in addition to one or two "key" genes, certain others, plus some sort of special stresses or environmental influences, must be present. However, the major hereditary difference between this disease and schizophrenia is that in schizophrenia, the predisposition to which is caused mainly by *recessive* genes, inheritance must come equally from *both* parents; but in manic-depressive insanity, since the "key" genes are at least *partly dominant,* there is a considerably greater threat to a child if only one parent is afflicted. Thus, in schizophrenia, if one parent has the disease, there is an up to one-in-six risk the child will develop it; but in manic-depressive insanity, if one parent is afflicted, the risk may be up to one in three that a child will develop the condition. Also, because the manic-depressive condition usually comes on later in life, it may take a longer time to know if any tendency has been inherited. Finally, the fact that this disease is different in nature and inheritance from schizophrenia has a special significance: If only the one type of mental disease has appeared on one side of a family, and only the other type on the other side, the threat of insanity to offspring is very much less than if the same afflictions had appeared on both sides.

HUNTINGTON'S CHOREA. This rare, but terrible mental disease, completely unrelated to any of the common types of insanity, is directly inherited through a *single dominant gene.* It is one of the most dreadful of all human afflictions, striking at a person in maturity—usually in the thirties or early forties—and from then on causing its victim literally to go to pieces in mind and body, with no known hope of cure, and ending in death after a few years. The worst feature of Huntington's chorea is that, since it is *dominant* in inheritance and comes on so far along in life, any child of a man or woman with the disease has a one-in-two chance of developing it, but may not know whether he will or will not until almost middle age. Tests now being developed may make it possible to reveal before maturity those who have inherited this dreadful gene, which, if they could then be induced to forego having children of their own, would greatly reduce the chance of the gene's being passed along. As it is, there is the grim fact that more than a thousand of the cases of Huntington's chorea in the United States in the past three centuries had their origin in genes carried by three brothers who came from England in pre-Revolutionary times; and that during the past century, in Minnesota alone, more than a hundred cases of the disease have appeared or are on their way to appearing among descendants of one afflicted man born in 1831. (One of the most disturbing facts, Dr. Sheldon Reed has shown, is that in American families where the disease has appeared, the afflicted persons have produced twice as many children as their unafflicted relatives.)

▶ *Pick's disease (lobar atrophy)*. Another very rare disease which, like Huntington's chorea, begins suddenly to cause deterioration of the brain and body in middle life, and is also inherited through a *single dominant gene*.

PSYCHOPATHIC PERSONALITY. This is a subtle and often not easily recognized type of mental disease which may cause great suffering, much more to the families of those afflicted and to society at large than to the diseased persons themselves. Psychopaths may often seem to be no more than "peculiar" persons —rather cold, selfish and immature—given to lying, deception and cheating, and to behavior which under certain conditions may lead to vicious and criminal acts. Fortunately, in other cases psychopaths with brilliant minds and talents may turn their energies into important and useful achievement. The fact that the true psychopath usually gives evidence of his peculiarities in early childhood, and often when there is little or nothing wrong in the environment, leads to the theory that some hereditary quirk is involved. The possibility of some brain disorder as one factor arises from recent reports that a majority of psychopaths have abnormal brain waves.

Neuroses. These include many personality disorders and psychological disturbances found in people who can be classed as fully "sane." There is much to indicate that ordinary "neurotic" behavior is largely the result of emotional stresses and difficult situations. But it is also not unlikely that heredity predisposes some persons more than others to become neurotic under given conditions. This is suggested by experiments with mice, rabbits and other lower animals, which show that those of certain breeds are especially prone to develop neuroses when exposed to stresses and conflicts. Also, there is limited recent evidence of psychoneurotic traits (including pathological fears, anxieties and hysteria), running so strongly in some human families that some investigators think a predisposition to such symptoms may be dominant in inheritance. In any case, since environment certainly, and heredity probably are involved, a fair conclusion is that when parents are definitely of the "neurotic" type, there is a considerably above average chance that their offspring will become so.

SUICIDE. Although this is often a completely rational (if not justifiable) act, perhaps as many as half the suicides in the United States are linked with some kind of mental instability or disease (most often manic-depressive insanity, sometimes schizophrenia—particularly in young people). To the extent, then, that heredity may be involved in the mental condition, it may be playing a part in some suicides and the possible repetitions of the act in some families. However, there is much to prove that even if there might be any predisposition to suicide, the act itself is largely dependent on environmental factors. Thus, the suicide rate as a whole in any group, community or country, or at different times, is directly related to 1) strains which make living less tolerable or bearable (as in depression periods, or during the horror reigns in Europe); 2) the degree of social or religious approval of suicide (the rate being far lower where suicide is condemned, as in Ireland, than where it is sanctioned, as in Japan); and 3) the extent to which in any group individuals are isolated from others and, in periods of distress, can or cannot find help and understanding.

▶ *Sex differences.* One of the most important facts about suicide is that almost everywhere in the world the rate among men is higher than among women—by about four times in the United States, where among Whites, sixteen per one thousand males and four per thousand females end their own lives. (Among Negroes the rate is far less—four per one thousand males, one per thousand females.) Chief reasons: 1) Men are under greater pressure to be successful, useful, physically active and independent, and when they fail in these respects, are more impelled toward suicide. 2) By inheritance, as we have seen, males are much more likely to suffer from diseases and defects. 3) There is some evidence that women inherently have better "shock absorbers," which can cushion them better against emotional upsets, disasters, and pain. Also, 4) psychoanalysts might maintain that insofar as self-destruction is aggression turned inwardly, males, being naturally more aggressive and given to violence, than females, would more often commit suicide. (See also *Sex differences in crime,* Chap. 23.)

Other Types of Abnormal Behavior: See also Chaps. 21 (*Behavior*); 22 (*Personality*); 23 (*Crime*); 24 (*Sexual behavior*).

17
Feeble-Mindedness
and Idiocy

WHO ARE THE "FEEBLE-MINDED"? When a person's mind is so slow moving and retarded that he is unable to learn, think, work and live in a normal way, he is classed as "feeble-minded"—the general term for all *mental defectives*. (As explained in the preceding chapter, "mental defect" is entirely different from "mental disease," or insanity.) Perhaps one in every forty children and adults is in the "feeble-minded" group. Included are various grades and types of defectives which should not be confused with one another, and which may be due to quite different causes, particularly so far as heredity is concerned.

▶ *"IQ" classification.* Technically, the grades of mental defectives are decided by the levels of intelligence they can reach, as measured by their "IQs" on various tests (usually the Stanford-Binet). A person is not classed as feeble-minded unless his IQ falls below 70. In turn, the feeble-minded are graded as follows: *Morons,* IQs of 69 down to 50; *imbeciles,* IQs of 50 down to 20; *idiots,* IQs of 20 or less. There also are important physical distinctions. The morons as a rule are defective only in intelligence, but with no physical abnormalities, injuries or diseases to explain their condition. In the idiots and imbeciles, however, defects in bodily functions and physical makeup often go with and may be the cause of the defects in their minds. Moreover, while heredity may play a major part in producing many if not most of the morons, it is much less responsible for the idiots and imbeciles (except some of the rare types). Finally, as we shall see, the risk of having a moron child is closely related to the parents' intelligence (being least for parents with high IQs, and highest for those of low IQs), whereas the risk of having an

137

idiot or imbecile child is almost the same for parents of high intelligence as for morons.

MORONS. These make up by far the largest proportion—perhaps seven in eight—of the mental defectives. The great majority of morons are physically normal or average, and in only a minority can mental backwardness be traced to environmental causes, such as disease, lack of proper care and training, or learning difficulties unrelated to intelligence. However, in borderline cases mistakes are sometimes made in wrongly grading persons as morons, either because of errors in test scores, or because the tests may fail to measure all phases of intelligence correctly. Thus, a child who may fall down badly on some or many parts of the standard intelligence tests (especially those related to "school" learning), may be quite average or even above average with respect to certain mental capacities and skills. Many persons rated as "morons" by their IQs prove efficient at various jobs, and make good social adjustments.

▶ *Hereditary factors.* Where no environmental causes are evident, many authorities believe that morons result mainly from inheritance of "slow-mind" genes which keep the brain from functioning beyond a certain degree of efficiency. The best theory is that these genes are *"recessive-plus"*—a pair of recessives *plus* perhaps a dominant gene or genes. Backing this up are these facts: 1) Moron children are very rare among parents of normal or superior intelligence, and very frequent among parents of low intelligence—more than three fourths of the morons coming from one tenth of the families. 2) If both parents are morons, the chance is anywhere from 60 to 75 per cent that a given child will be, whereas with parents of normal IQs it may be no more than 1 or 2 per cent, and with parents of above-average IQs very much less. 3) Once a moron child has been born to two parents, the chance is about one in eight—five times the average—that they will have another retarded child. 4) Among identical twins, if one is a moron, so is the other in almost every case, whereas among fraternal twins this is true in less than half, and perhaps only one fourth of the cases.

▶ *"Pseudo-feeble-mindedness."* This refers to infrequent cases of children with normal intelligence who are wrongly classed as "morons" when parents and teachers are unaware that their backwardness is due to reading difficulties, speech or hearing defects, diseases, or emotional blocks. The mistake is most often made when difficulties of this nature are minor ones and not easily recognized. Careful tests by trained psychologists will easily distinguish the "pseudo" from the true feeble-minded children, and make possible corrective measures.

▶ *"Curing" morons?* Reports from time to time of "phenomenal" improvements or cures of feeble-minded children through this or that treatment must be accepted with extreme caution. In some cases a marked increase in a child's IQ, or mental performance may follow if he was originally wrongly scored, or if his backwardness was of the "pseudo" type just discussed. But once it is definitely known that the child's defect centers in a "slow" brain, the only thing that can be done (so far as science now knows) is to provide training which will make the most of his limited capacities. To date none of the much-publicized treatments or "cures," as with glutamic acid, thiamin or other chemicals, have been proved effective.

IMBECILES AND IDIOTS. These, as previously noted, are defectives with IQs no higher than 50—from 50 down to 20 for imbeciles, and below 20 for idiots. Many in both groups also have physical abnormalities or peculiarities usually recognizable at birth, although in some in-between cases the symptoms may not be conclusive until the baby is several years old. The large majority of the imbeciles and idiots result mostly from deficiencies or other unfavorable factors in the prenatal environment, with heredity possibly contributing. (Only in the less common cases is heredity the sole and direct cause.) Despite popular notions, very few cases of idiocy—probably less than one in a hundred—are due to birth injuries, and perhaps no more than another one per cent result from falls on the head or other accidents in infancy and childhood. Among the stillborn or miscarried babies who are malformed and defective, it is probable that a considerable percentage would be idiots or imbeciles if they could survive. As it is, the death rates among the low-grade mental defectives both prenatally and in the first years of life is very high, so that those who live to puberty or beyond may represent only a minority.

Mongolian Idiots (or imbeciles, depending on the level of intelligence reached). These comprise the largest group—about 20 per cent—of all the feeble-minded below the moron level. Out of every thousand babies born, perhaps two or more are "mongoloids." The condition gets its name from the peculiar type of eyes, with folds at the corners somewhat as in the Mongolian peoples, which originally led to the mistaken notion that such babies were throwbacks to remote Mongolian ancestors. But there is no racial connection whatsoever; these idiots may be born to parents of all stocks. Going with the odd eyes are usually a great many other abnormalities; in the nose, forehead, ears, tongue, voice, hands, palm-prints, etc. There may also be organic defects, which cause many mongoloid babies to die in infancy or childhood. If they survive and pass puberty—some of them living well into middle age—they remain stunted in growth and, usually, sexually undeveloped. (Few mongoloids have children.)

▶ *Causes.* While still uncertain, most authorities believe Mongolian idiocy results from some glandular disorder or deficiency in the mother which throws the child's development off its proper course in the very first stages of prenatal life. The older the mother, the more likely this is to happen. Although young mothers, too, sometimes produce such babies, almost half are born to mothers over forty. Among mothers under thirty the incidence of mongoloid babies is less than one per thousand; it rises from that age on, sharply as the forties approach, and among mothers *over forty-five,* the rate is one mongoloid baby in every thirty-five to forty births.

▶ *Heredity in Mongolism?* While there has to be something wrong in the prenatal environment to cause Mongolian idiocy, hereditary factors possibly contribute to the chances that it will develop. One theory is that heredity may predispose certain mothers to create this wrong environment for their babies; another theory, that some inherited weakness may cause certain babies to be particularly susceptible to development of the condition. The evidence, not too strong, is based on the frequency of Mongolian idiots in some family groups, and the fact that among identical twins, when one is mongoloid the other is also so almost invariably, which is not true of fraternal twins. However, it is rare for two mongoloids to be born to the same mother, which supports the conclusion that the factors causing the condition are highly complex and unpredictable.

Cretinism. This type of mental defect is clearly caused in prenatal life by a thyroid deficiency in the mother (often if she is goiterous), which stunts the baby's mental and physical development and produces various other abnormalities. In maturity cretins still look like odd little children, with large heads, pot bellies, pug noses, thick lips and protruding tongues. Cretinism sometimes runs in families, but whether heredity plays any part in this is uncertain. If it does, an unproved theory is that it is by way of recessive genes which either produce some thyroid deficiency in the mother, or some special susceptibility in the child. (See also "Goiter," Chap. 12.)

Microcephalic Idiocy. In this condition the individual has an abnormally small head ("pinhead"), which results from an early stoppage in the growth of the brain and the skull. Some cases of microcephaly are inherited through *recessive* genes, which may lead to several children of this type appearing in one family. But the condition may also be largely or entirely environmental, produced by various prenatal deficiencies or upsets. An occasional cause in recent years has been undue exposure of pregnant mothers to X-rays, a factor likely to increase in menacing importance if there is atomic warfare.

Hydrocephaly ("water head"). In this condition the head is swollen abnormally by fluid in the brain, which often results in mental defect but sometimes does not, especially if there is proper early treatment (including drainage of the fluid). The condition has been found inherited in certain lower animals, and there is a possibility that some (but not all) of the cases in humans may also be hereditary, perhaps through a dominant-qualified gene.

Amaurotic family idiocy. There are several types and degrees of this condition, all inherited through *recessive* genes, which cause fatty swellings in the nerve cells of the brain and spinal cord, leading to idiocy, blindness and paralysis. The most common and most severe type is in infants, and brings early death. Milder types may develop in childhood or maturity.

Gargoylism. A rare, complex, inherited condition, probably due to *recessive* (in some cases sex-linked) genes which seriously disturb the afflicted child's chemical processes, and cause idiocy, distorted features, dwarfism and many other abnormalities.

Phenylpyruvic idiocy. An unusual type of inherited idiocy, due to a serious chemical disorder in prenatal life which shows itself after birth through the excretion of phenylpyruvic acid in the urine. The condition is *simple-recessive*, which means that where parents have had one such child, there is a clear one-in-four risk of having another. Recent experiments hold out hope that mental functioning in this condition may be improved through chemical treatment.

Laurence-Moon syndrome. A complex condition in which there is idiocy, mental defect, eye defect, extra fingers and other abnormalities. Rec.-Q. in inheritance.

Epiloia. See under *Rare skin cancers,* Chap. 12.

Epilepsy. Although previously discussed at length in Chapter 14, epilepsy is also mentioned here because in about 10 per cent of the cases it is accompanied by feeble-mindedness. This may happen only when the condition, which is primarily an ailment of the nervous system, affects the brain so as to retard its workings. In the great majority of cases, however, epilepsy has no such effect, and the afflicted persons are mentally completely normal and sometimes even brilliant.

18

Length of Life

ONE'S "ALLOTTED" YEARS. Many people, past and present, have held to the belief that everyone has an allotted number of years of life. Thus, soldiers say, "You'll go when your number's up." This fatalistic view is hardly valid. What is true, however, is that human beings, first as a species—like all other species of animals—and second, as individuals, do have a "number" set by their heredity for the maximum years that they can live. This "number" for humans generally, so far as we know now, is greater than for any other living creatures, except the giant tortoises and turtles which may live to ages of 180 or more. The Bible speaks of humans who lived to much longer "years" (Adam, 930, Methuselah, 969, Cainan, 910, etc.), but authorities believe these pre-Flood biblical "years" may have referred to periods little more than a tenth of our modern years. Also it is believed that the ages of post-Flood biblical personages (Abraham, 175, Isaac, 180, etc.) were computed by systems different from those by which we reckon years today. It is significant that at a later stage the Bible referred to man's allotted years as "three score and ten" (70), which—by coincidence or not—is almost exactly the average expectation of life in the United States today.

▶ *Modern longevity records.* As in the past, reports continue to appear from time to time of persons supposedly living to the age of 130, 140, 150, etc. Almost invariably these persons are from remote backward regions or countries, with no authentic records to support their claims. Actually, proved human longevity records of modern times do not go beyond the age of 115. Moreover, despite the fact that we are living in the most favorable period for longevity in the world's history, only about four

143

persons in 100,000 are reaching or passing the age of one hundred.

Increases in longevity. Taking present life spans in the United States, from birth to death, people as a whole are now living almost a third longer than they did at the beginning of the century, and almost twice as long as in George Washington's time. That is, if we compare the present life expectancy at birth of almost seventy years, with the average expectancy in 1900 of forty-eight years, and in Revolutionary times of about thirty-five. This tremendous gain has obviously not been because of any change in heredity, but solely because of the enormous improvement in health, living conditions and medical care. Mainly this has brought greatly reduced death rates in infancy, childhood and early maturity, enabling many more persons to live into the older ages. For people past middle life, however, the longevity chances are only a few years better than a half century ago, and for those reaching seventy, only about a year better, showing that despite environmental improvements, a general longevity time limit is still at work on human life spans.

INDIVIDUAL LONGEVITY CHANCES. Whatever the average longevity limits for humans may be, there is little doubt but that some individuals are geared by their hereditary makeup for longer "runs" or life spans than are others, given equal environmental conditions. Some of the ways in which "longevity" genes may work or be kept from working, have been suggested in the chapters on diseases and defects. In certain conditions there are "killer" genes (technically called *lethals*), which bring death almost before a life is under way; in other hereditary conditions death may be set to occur at various more or less definite periods, in childhood, at puberty, in early maturity or before middle age. Less directly, there are various hereditary defects or weaknesses affecting the heart and arteries, kidneys and other vital organs, the nervous system, body tissues, etc., which may decrease individuals' survival chances. Predispositions to mental disease may also curtail longevity chances by adversely affecting the person's way of living, or inducing suicide. Finally, different gene-combinations undoubtedly tend to construct the bodies and influence the general functioning of individuals in different ways, all of which have a bearing on the rates of wear and tear, disease resistance, aging and risks of vital breakdowns. Thus, insofar as their genes may differ, no two individuals start out with exactly the same longevity chances. But the best of heredity can only give a person the possibility of living until such and such an age if the conditions are right. A sudden accident can cancel out all the effects of "long-life" genes.

▶ *Twin studies.* Some clues as to the relative importance of heredity and environment on people's life spans are offered by the twin studies of Dr. Franz Kallmann and others. Tentative findings are that identical twins are much closer in their ages lived and in the symptoms of aging than are fraternals. So far, of the completed lives on record, identical twins died only three years apart on the average; fraternal twins died more than six years apart.

Long-Lived families. As we have seen, we may make some guesses about a person's "longevity" genes by knowing what hereditary defects he may or may not have. But also important may be the longevity records of his parents, grandparents and other near relatives, because various studies have indicated that tendencies to longer or shorter life spans run in families under the same outside conditions. Mostly the differences are related to the incidences of death from major diseases. For instance, a recent (1954) study by life-insurance companies shows that persons two or more members of whose immediate family died from heart and related conditions under age sixty, had about a 40 per cent higher than average death risk for their age. Family histories of diabetes, cancer, mental disease and other conditions also may affect individuals' longevity chances, unless it is clear that they themselves are free of the conditions. In general, persons both of whose parents were long-lived stand a better chance of reaching a ripe old age than do those with only one long-lived parent, and a much better chance than those with two short-lived parents. In every case, however, one must establish the causes of the parents' deaths: If due only to accident, infectious diseases or other purely environmental factors, their children's own longevity chances need obviously not be affected (unless they also were exposed to the same bad environmental factors).

At the same time, even if hereditary conditions played a part in the parents' deaths, many such conditions may now (or presently) be checked, restrained or cured by treatment. In either case, a family history of short life need not at all mean that any given member may not be long-lived.

SEX DIFFERENCES IN LONGEVITY. By far the most important general influence on any person's longevity chances is his or her sex. We have seen in earlier chapters how heredity works to make males much more likely than females to develop a great many diseases and defects which are "sex-linked" (with genes on the "X" chromosome), and also more vulnerable to many serious conditions which are not directly hereditary, but in which heredity may play a part, or to which the male system is particularly susceptible. This applies to virtually all major death-producing conditions except diabetes, exophthalmic goiter and gallstones, and, of course, the specifically female cancers. There also seem to be certain general factors in the female systems which enable them to stand up better under environmental hazards of many kinds—accidents, shocks, infections, starvation, etc. Thus, as brought out in Chapter 11 ("Males and Females"), long before there are any environmental differences for the two sexes, in prenatal life and in infancy, the male death rate is about 30 per cent higher. (It is worth noting that among almost all lower animals there is also an excess of male deaths in early life.) In childhood and youth there is a drop to 12 per cent more male than female deaths, but in maturity the male death rate climbs again to a 30 per cent margin over that of females. However, after early childhood a considerable part (though far from all) of the excess male death rate is caused by the male's greater exposure to accidents, war, occupational diseases and various other adverse factors. Throwing the longevity balance further toward females is the fact that improvements in environment, medical care and social conditions have benefited them relatively more than males. For one thing, deaths through childbearing have been cut to a small fraction of what they once were (now about one in two thousand births in the United States— or one twelfth the rate in 1915).

Male, female life expectancies. The foregoing facts show up clearly in the present estimates of years remaining for men and women of different ages. At birth today the life expectation for a male is about 66, for a female almost 72. At age 20 a man has about 49 more years of life expectancy, a young woman 54 more years. At age 30 the average man has about 40 years of life ahead of him, the average woman, 44½ years. At age 40 for men the expectancy is about 30.7 more years, for women 35 years. At age 50, the average man has about 22½ more years of life expectancy, the average woman almost 26½. At age 60, the expectancy for men is about 15.4 more years, for women 18.1 more years. The margin declines with the older ages, but always continues in favor of women. While these figures are for persons in the United States, they apply closely to those in other advanced countries as well. However, in less favored countries where poor environments bring high death rates, particularly in childbearing, women have almost as low life expectancies as men.

▶ *Numbers of men, women.* As we saw in Chapter 4, the sexes start off at birth with about 106 boys born to every 100 girls. From then on the higher death rate of males steadily reduces their excess numbers, so that in early maturity the male excess is virtually wiped out, and by middle life there are about 15 per cent more women. In the seventies there are 20 per cent more women, and from about ninety on, almost twice as many women as men surviving. These figures are for the United States. The excess of women at the different ages is even greater in England, Germany and France. But as stated before, in less advanced countries, where environments are bad, the excess of women is much less.

▶ *Chances of widowhood.* In two out of three cases now the husband is the first to die, whereas at the beginning of the century it was almost as likely to be the wife as the husband. The chance of widowhood for a woman increases, naturally, with the number of years that her husband is older. If the husband and wife are the same age, there is a 62 per cent chance he will die first; if he is five years older, there is a 70 per cent chance, and if he is ten years older, there is an 80 per cent chance. Because of the higher death rate of males at any given age, the husband must be more than five years younger than the wife before the odds are in favor of his surviving her. On the average today when women in the United States become widows they are about fifty-six years old, and three quarters of them live on for another twenty years.

GROUP DIFFERENCES IN LONGEVITY. Many mistakes were formerly made in comparing "long-lived" and "short-lived" stocks, races, groups or classes of human beings, and ascribing their differences to "superior" or "inferior" hereditary makeup. As we have seen, heredity does tend to make many individuals and families longer lived than others, but this can be proved only when all the persons involved live under the same conditions. It is another matter when the environments differ greatly, for it may then be not the hereditary, but the environmental factors which account for the differences in longevity. Thus, one finds today (as there has always been) a fairly close relationship between longevity averages and the conditions existing among different groups in the same city, state or country, whatever their race or ethnic stock.

▶ *Race differences.* While racial groups may differ to some extent in their inherited susceptibility to various diseases and defects, there is no evidence that when all factors are taken together, people of any race are destined by heredity to outlive others. There is much to indicate that such racial longevity differences as there are, may be due mainly to environment. For instance, Negro life expectancies in the United States in 1900 were almost sixteen years less than those of Whites. But as conditions for Negroes improved, so did their life expectancies, until today their average longevity is only about six years less than that of Whites, and might eventually become the same. Already one may note that present Negro life expectancies are much higher than those of many White groups in other parts of the world today, or than the life expectancies of American Whites a half century ago.

▶ *Ethnic longevity differences.* Among European Whites, and

Husband-Wife Survival

(Based on current life expectancies in the United States)*

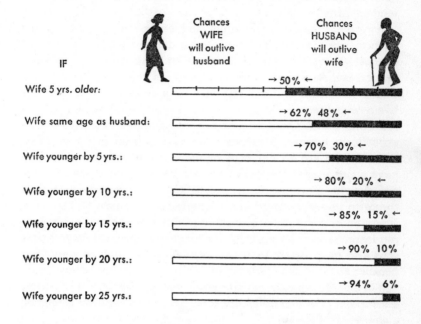

IF	Chances WIFE will outlive husband	Chances HUSBAND will outlive wife
Wife 5 yrs. older:	→ 50% ←	
Wife same age as husband:	→ 62%	48% ←
Wife younger by 5 yrs.:	→ 70%	30% ←
Wife younger by 10 yrs.:	→ 80%	20% ←
Wife younger by 15 yrs.:	→ 85%	15% ←
Wife younger by 20 yrs.:	→ 90%	10%
Wife younger by 25 yrs.:	→ 94%	6%

*Statistics compiled by Metropolitan Life Insurance Company.

among foreign-born Americans and their children, those of different stocks show differences both in longevity and in death rates from specific causes. For example, Irish-Americans have a considerably higher death rate than Italian-Americans, and there also are differences in their causes of death. In turn, other longevity and death-rate differences appear among Americans of English, Russian, Polish, German, Jewish and other ethnic origins. But since these groups differ from each other in living habits, diets and occupations, it is difficult to tell whether their longevity differences are due solely to environmental factors or whether (as some authorities believe) heredity also plays a part.

FACTORS IN INDIVIDUAL LONGEVITY. Within all groups—as classified by sex, family, race, ethnic origin or living standards—the longevity chances for given individuals have been found related to the following factors in which hereditary tendencies may be involved:

▶ *Personal health.* The chief influences on one's longevity chances are the absence or presence of the major degenerative diseases—heart and artery, kidney and lung diseases, diabetes, cancer, etc. Apart from these and some of the less common conditions known to be fatal, one may be a chronic invalid and yet live a long life.

▶ *Body build.* One's weight has considerable bearing on life-expectancy because it worsens the threats from many diseases. Persons who are 25 per cent or more overweight for their age have a death rate about 75 per cent higher than those of average weight. Extreme underweight in young people also is a threat to life-expectancy, but perhaps only because it often is a symptom of some disease or internal disorder. Among older people leanness may be an asset for longevity. Moderately tall persons also have better than average longevity chances—probably because those in the more favored groups tend to be above average in height. But extreme tallness (well over seven feet) is often a symptom of a glandular disorder, and may carry the threat of a shortened life span.

▶ *Blood pressure and pulse.* The higher one's blood pressure, the shorter the life expectancy, as a rule, because of the association with heart-arterial-kidney diseases. Low blood pressure (if not extremely low) may be a longevity asset. Too rapid pulse (near or over 100 per minute) or very irregular pulse, may also decrease longevity chances, particularly if there is overweight or hypertension. Heart murmurs of certain types (functional— "inconstant apical," or "systolic pulmonic") are quite harmless, but other types of heart murmurs (organic), are symptomatic of various heart diseases, which are possible life-shorteners.

▶ *Occupation.* The more one's job affords opportunities for healthy and careful living, the better the longevity chances, from extra months to extra years. As groups, the longest-lived are professional people—clergymen, teachers, lawyers, and engineers, with doctors having somewhat shorter life-expectancies. Next in longevity are business executives, white-collar workers, skilled workers. Writers, artists and musicians as a group have somewhat shorter than average life spans. Shortest-lived are unskilled workers, miners, quarrymen and others exposed to irritating dusts and other disease hazards; itinerant workers characterized by hard-living, careless habits; and men in various dangerous occupations. Farmers are hard to classify because they are of different levels, their life-expectancies going with their living conditions, but in general they are among the longest-lived persons either because their work is more healthful, or because they have to be healthy to be farmers.

▶ *Temperament and habits.* Persons who are excitable and fast-living do not as a rule live as long as the placid and easy-going ones, and in this heredity may play some part. (In lower animals, too, the most active species and breeds, which burn up the most energy, tend to be the shorter-lived.) Excessive smoking and drinking, to the extent that they go with tenseness and instability (hereditary or otherwise), may also be life-shorteners. But in some individuals moderate drinking and/or moderate smoking may be relaxing and not detrimental to longevity.

Extending Human Life Spans. How much farther longevity of human beings can be extended is highly uncertain. Apart from the general improvements in environment and medical care, no "life-prolonging" or "rejuvenating" methods have yet proved to be successful. This applies to hormone treatments, rejuvenating "serums," diets or foods of one kind or another. Perhaps the average longevity may in a generation or two reach seventy-five for women and seventy for men. But whether it can go much beyond that, or whether any human individuals can be enabled to live to ages of 120 or over, depends entirely on what limits have been set by human heredity. These limits are still anyone's guess.

19

Intelligence

HOW MUCH IS INHERITED? If heredity produces different degrees of abnormal and low intelligence (Chaps. 16, 17), should it not also produce different degrees of *normal* and *superior* intelligence? Undoubtedly it does, for variations in intelligence are no less subject to the workings of genes than are variations in size or stature, or in physical functions. We see this most clearly in comparing the mental capacities of human beings and of lower animals, and often, the responses of various breeds within a given species, such as dogs. There can be no argument that these differences are overwhelmingly due to heredity. What is at issue is only whether—or to what extent—the relatively small differences in normal intelligence among human beings themselves are also produced by heredity. This, as we shall see, is extremely hard to establish, because human intelligence is far more complex than it was formerly thought to be, and is so greatly subject to environmental influences. Nevertheless, even the limited evidence available is sufficient to refute many wrong beliefs about human minds and to make clear how heredity and environment interact to influence them.

▶ *Judging "intelligence."* In everyday life we rate people as "brilliant," "bright," "ordinary," "stupid," etc. But even if these offhand ratings are correct, psychologists are well aware that the intelligence *shown* by an individual does not necessarily reflect the true quality of his mind. Many persons never had or have the chance to develop their mental capacities fully, and are frequently misjudged because of the common tendency to confuse intelligence with *education.* Thus, before we can tell what role heredity plays in human mentality, we must have scientific standards for measuring it.

▶ *What is "intelligence"?* There is increasing awareness that intelligence is not a single trait, as was formerly thought, but a combination of a great many traits and capacities. Among them are abstract thinking, quickness of learning, memory, word fluency, language comprehension, arithmetical ability, speed of judgment, ability to visualize shapes and spaces, ability to "sense" people, "intuition," etc. The different elements of intelligence may not go together in the same persons, which helps to explain why some are bright or capable in certain ways and not in others. (*Special talents:* Chap. 20, following.)

▶ *"Brain" genes.* Since intelligence is compounded of many capacities, a great many genes undoubtedly contribute to its quality and type. Most probably there are, first, a large number of genes, in different orders of importance, which govern the general construction of the brain and brain cells, their functioning, and their "hookups" with the sensory organs and other parts of the nervous system. Second, there are additional genes involved in particular processes relating to specific mental traits and abilities. But this must remain theoretical until these "mental" genes are identified and their effects determined.

INTELLIGENCE TESTS. The various widely used intelligence tests are extremely helpful in measuring the relative mental *performances* of individuals. But how far the tests also dig beneath environmental influences and measure inborn mental *capacities* is a question. Actually, the standard tests (such as the Stanford-Binet) measure mainly the "academic" abilities, required for mastering the usual school subjects. Other tests also help to measure special abilities needed for given tasks, jobs and professions. Where the tests so far are weakest is in measurement of 1) "social intelligence," involved in understanding other people and getting along with them; 2) traits such as "drive," curiosity, sense of humor, shrewdness, or "intuition"; and 3) unusual qualities of the mind involved in "creativeness," "originality" or mechanical ability, needed in many fields. (Chap. 20.)

▶ *"IQ" scores.* These are derived through two kinds of tests, one for children, one for adults. The IQs of children, through age sixteen, are determined by how well or poorly a child does in comparison with the average for his age. In Chapter 17 there

were given the subnormal IQ ratings under 70, for idiots, imbeciles and morons. IQs of 70 to 80 are in the "borderline"
group. Beyond these, individuals are classified by IQs as follows:
80 to 90, "dull-normal"; 90 to 110, "normal"; 110-120, "superior";
120-140, "very superior"; 140 or over, "genius" (only in the technical "IQ" sense, but not as applied to the true and extremely
rare geniuses to be dealt with in Chapter 20).

▶ *Adult IQs.* Psychologists have long gone on the assumption
that intelligence becomes "set" toward the end of adolescence.
For this reason, the intelligence tests for persons of all ages after
sixteen made little allowance for age. Any advantages of younger
adults on some parts of the tests, because of quicker minds and
better memory, were considered offset on other parts of the tests
by older persons' greater store of acquired knowledge and experience. Recently, however, Dr. David Wechsler, after extensive researches leading to preparation of new tests for adults,
concluded that intelligence, (as measured by test performance),
increases from adolescence until age twenty-five or even age
thirty, and then declines slightly from year to year. The new
Wechsler Adult Intelligence Test, therefore, makes allowance
for age differences. But as with children's IQs, there is still much
uncertainty as to how closely adult test scores reflect basic or all-
around intelligence.

▶ *Variations in IQs.* The same person's IQ may sometimes be
given as different by several points (up to 10 or more) on tests
in successive years, or even within a few weeks or months. This
may be because of differences in the tests or test methods, or in
the examiners, or in the person's state of health, energy and degrees of application. In very young normal children (under five),
IQs are not too easily or reliably determined. (Unrecognized
reading or hearing difficulties, emotional and psychological
blocks, and sometimes physical factors, may occasionally impede
a young child's mental performance, or cause it to vary greatly
from one year to another.) But at older ages an individual's IQ
ordinarily tends to remain fairly constant from year to year.

▶ *IQs and achievement.* To the extent that IQs are not always
true measures of mental capacities, they may also not be accurate forecasts of future success or failure. Nevertheless, IQs

are becoming more and more important in determining how children will be educated, and which students will be admitted to the more selective colleges and accepted for medical and other professional schools. IQs and other test scores also are being used in engaging workers for various jobs in industries, and by the armed forces in choosing men for special training and advancement. Thus, IQs and the opportunities for achievement, if not achievement itself, are becoming more closely related. As one example, the large group of high IQ (150 average) individuals who as children began to be studied by Professor Lewis M. Terman in 1921, and who have been followed up since, have for the most part continued to be outstanding both in IQs and in achievements. On the other hand, to prove that a high IQ alone does not insure success, a number of persons in this group failed in college and ended up in lowly jobs. (*See also:* Chap. 20, *Prodigies.*)

IQS AND INHERITANCE: Parents and Children. Studies of the inheritance of human intelligence so far depend mainly on comparisons of the IQs of parents and children, and of identical and fraternal twins in relation to non-twin brothers and sisters. Taking up the first relationship, there is much evidence that IQs of children, on the average, are fairly close to those of their parents. In individual instances this may not be so, but taking families collectively, parents with high IQs tend to have children of well-above-average brightness, and rarely a dull child (except for the defective cases discussed in Chapter 17). In the opposite direction, parents with low IQs, as a group, tend to have low-IQ children, and only very rarely a brilliant child. (See also concluding section of this chapter.)

▶ *Parents' professions: children's IQs.* Supporting what has been said, various studies show that IQs of children of men engaged in the "brainier" jobs tend to be higher than those of men in jobs requiring less mental ability. Thus, children of professional men have IQs averaging 116; of semi-professional men and business executives, 112; of upper white-collar men, most businessmen, and skilled workers, 107; of clerks, minor business people and semi-skilled workers, 104; of slightly skilled workers, 97; of day laborers, 96. (Figures for the United States, but closely paralleled in England and other countries, including the Soviet Union.)

▶ *Bias in the studies?* How far the facts presented prove inheritance of intelligence depends on the fairness of the tests for the different groups. There is some evidence that the IQ tests may indeed be slanted toward the kind of learning acquired by children from the more educated and more privileged homes. Therefore these children would tend to score higher IQs than less privileged children, even if hereditary factors were equal. Yet it cannot be ignored that the mental environments provided for children are in themselves considerably influenced by how basically intelligent or unintelligent their parents are. Allowing for all biases, then, the relationships between parents' and children's IQs very likely reflect the influence of both heredity and environment.

Twin and Sibling IQs. Added proof of the role of heredity in intelligence is seen in findings that the IQ differences between identical (one-egg) twins are quite small (5.9 points), and even when *reared apart* average 7.7 points, whereas the IQ differences between fraternal (two-egg) twins *reared together* average 8.4 points, and between non-twin siblings (brothers or sisters) reared together, 14.5 points. However, about one in twenty identical twins (including some reared together) differ in IQ by 15 points or more, indicating how much environment can affect intelligence-test scores.

Orphaned brothers and sisters. Studies made in orphanages some years ago showed a much closer relationship between the IQs of brothers and/or sisters in the same institution than between unrelated children, even though all were in the same environments, and regardless of how long they'd been there.

Adopted children. There is uncertainty as to the degree to which the IQs of adopted children tend to follow those of their true parents or of their foster parents. Conflicting findings are due to special difficulties in making this type of study. One can hardly doubt that an adopted child's IQ will be influenced by the care, training and education he or she receives. But perhaps the majority of experts would hold that if two adopted children were reared in the same home in the same way, a child whose true parents were mentally superior would be considerably more likely to show high intelligence than would a child whose true parents were mentally only average, or below average.

BODY AND MIND. Among normal individuals in general, there is little indication that the "mental" genes are linked with genes for physical traits, or that under ordinary circumstances the bodily condition affects the IQ by more than a few points either way. Although present-day children are on the average much healthier, and taller for their ages, than were children of previous generations (and, often, than their parents were), few would maintain that they are brighter. Nor have persons in Europe today who as children during World War II suffered the most extreme hardships and the scantiest diets, turned out to be any less intelligent than those reared under the best conditions elsewhere. Going far back, the cave men of fifty thousand years ago, scientists believe, had as much brain power as modern human beings, despite enormous differences in health, diet and physical makeup.

▶ *Head or brain size, and IQ.* Popular notions that the size of the head, forehead or brain offers a good clue to a person's intelligence, have little scientific support. As between lower animals and human beings the very great differences in brain size and structure (particularly in the forepart, the *cerebral cortex*), do go with their relative mental capacities. But among human beings themselves the sizes of brains (other than in abnormal cases, such as of microcephalic or "pinhead," idiots) are of little significance as compared with their qualitative structure and functioning. Whites, for instance, have smaller brains on the average than Eskimos; some geniuses have had big heads, some small heads; and many prehistoric men had bigger brains than modern men. As it is, no brain specialist can yet tell from the size, shape or convolutions of a normal brain how intelligent an individual might be or was.

MALE AND FEMALE INTELLIGENCE. Where bodily factors working in a highly complex way may possibly affect intelligence in the *direction* it takes, if not its *quantity*, is in the sexes. Within any group, anywhere, one can find important differences in mental qualities and performances between boys and girls, men and women. But since the environments, rearing, objectives and roles of the two sexes are not and never can be completely the same, one cannot expect to measure accurately their mental capacities on the same scale or to prove that either sex is superior, inferior or even precisely equal in total intelligence to the other. Only in their performances on specific mental tasks can the sexes be properly compared. Here are some findings:

▶ *Girls* from the earliest ages are consistently better in finger dexterity (lacing shoes, dressing themselves, etc.); in tests involving language (little girls begin to talk earlier than do boys, as a rule, and many fewer girls have speech difficulties); reading and writing; memory (of songs, and of what they've read); esthetic responses (matching shapes and colors); and "sensing" people and noting details about them. In high school and college, girls continue to be superior in verbal tests and modern foreign languages (but not Latin).

▶ *Boys* are consistently superior as a group in abstract reasoning, mathematics, mechanical ability, structural skills and curiosity about the way things are put together, or what is happening outside of them. As they go on into college, boys excel in the sciences, mathematics, history, civics and economics. Also, in groups starting out with the same high IQs or scholarship levels, more boys remain at the high level, more girls drop behind.

▶ *What causes these sex differences?* Recent studies throw doubt on previous theories that all the sex differences in mental performance are due to "social conditioning." As we saw in previous discussions of sex differences, the "XX" and "XY" chromosome mechanisms set off the development of numerous differences between the sexes in biological makeup and functioning (Chap. 9, *features;* Chap. 10, *shape and stature;* Chaps. 11, 12, 13, 14, *defects, diseases and abnormalities;* Chap. 18, *longevity*). There is every reason why inborn sex differences would also influence the mental processes, but how or to what extent they do so awaits proof. One fact should not be overlooked: As education and training of women has more closely approached that of men, and their opportunities for jobs and service have been extended, they have shown capacities in many fields for which their "minds" were previously thought unfitted. (*See also:* Chap. 20, "Sex Differences In Achievement.")

RACE DIFFERENCES IN INTELLIGENCE. Whatever differences might currently be found in the thinking and mental achievements of persons of different races and nationalities, there is no way yet of proving that these are inborn. The chief reason, as already indicated, is that the available intelligence tests cannot be fairly and equally applied to groups of people reared, educated and living under markedly different conditions. Further, since the standard tests were mainly devised by and for White Europeans and Americans, they may discriminate against individuals of other races and nationalities.

▶ *Negro and White intelligence.* The foregoing observations apply particularly to any findings that average IQs of Negroes are below those of Whites. An unquestioned fact is that environments and learning opportunities of Negroes have for generations been inferior to those of Whites, and despite great advances in recent years, still are. Wherever Negroes enjoy relatively more equality and more opportunity for education, their IQs average considerably higher than in areas where they are repressed. In fact, among American Army draftees in World War II, Negroes from some Northern states had considerably lower rejection rates for substandard intelligence than had Whites from some Southern states. There also has been a marked increase in the relative numbers of Negro children with high IQs (140 to 150 or over), and in Negro individuals reaching top professional ranks. Most authorities feel that until environments are fully equalized, no valid conclusions can be drawn about the relative IQs or mental capacities of Whites and Negroes, or those of other races.

CONCLUSIONS. Despite the uncertainties dealt with in this chapter, these conclusions are justified:

1. The intelligence any person *shows* is always the combined result of his heredity and his environment.

2. *Physical* influences (health, diet, climate, comforts, etc.) are less likely to affect a person's mental performance than are *psychological* influences and opportunities for learning.

3. The inherited mental factors are so numerous, of so many

kinds, work in such complex ways, and are so difficult to determine and measure, that no precise predictions can be made about the transmission of intelligence from parents to children according to any such ratios or formulas as are possible with respect to many simpler traits.

4. What can only be said is that high intelligence, judged by *both* high IQ and achievement, signifies the presence of superior "mental" genes. If both parents are of this type, the children are more likely to start off with superior mental equipment than if only one parent shows high intelligence, and much more so than if neither parent is mentally outstanding. However, where parents are exceptionally brilliant, the odds are that the children will not quite approach their mental levels. (See Chap. 20, "*The 'genius' genes.*") On the other hand, parents of below-average IQs may well have children with IQs averaging considerably higher than theirs, particularly if the parents had lacked opportunities for adequate mental development.

5. It may never be possible to draw conclusions about the inheritance of a person's *whole* intelligence. But it may eventually be quite possible to measure and predict the inheritance of separate elements of intelligence, or of different mental abilities and capacities, each of which may be influenced by different genes. (*Further discussions in the next chapter.*)

20

Talent and Genius

DIFFERENCES IN ABILITY. Most people find out in the course of time that they are good at certain things and not at others. Alert parents will notice children showing special talents at early ages, and will also be aware that one child may differ markedly from another in given abilities. What causes these differences? A first important fact is that special aptitudes or talents need not be related to intelligence. A person may be good at music, painting, writing, knitting, pie-baking or what not, and yet be much less bright than someone who is a bungler at the same specialty. Again, different abilities may or may not be related to one another. Some persons are good at many things, others seem to be good at only one thing. And for any given ability, there may be a range from up to "phenomenal" down to nearly zero. All this would suggest that just as there are genes which govern a person's capacity to develop physically and mentally in various ways, there may be genes which govern or influence his capacity to develop special abilities. However, we are just beginning to identify particular "talent" genes and to evolve theories as to how they work—always keeping in mind that the expression of any talent can be much influenced by environment.

MUSICAL TALENT. Of all human talents, this gives the clearest evidence of heredity because it reveals itself most spontaneously, at the earliest ages, and in all sorts of environments, and because there is abundant evidence that it runs brilliantly in particular families. Further, in musical *performance*, the talent of one individual can be much more easily compared with that of another than is the case in other arts and fields of achievement. (Many of the facts which follow are derived from the author's own study of the talent backgrounds of large groups of

161

outstanding musical virtuosi and opera singers. The study, made in 1938, is reported in detail in the author's book, "You and Heredity," and is summarized in *"The New* You and Heredity.")

▶ *Precociousness.* In almost every case great musical talent expresses itself before the age of five or six, and often as early as age two or three. It may appear without any training, being revealed through singing, humming or response to music, sometimes in a baby who has not yet learned to talk. Many authorities believe that if marked musical ability is not definitely revealed, or cannot be detected, in the very early years, there is little likelihood that it will be developed later.

▶ *Family backgrounds.* Usually there is marked talent in parents and/or near-relatives of great musicians. But as proof that a musical home is not of itself the determining factor, some of the greatest virtuosi came from untalented families, and many brilliant musicians have found regretfully that their children, despite the finest musical environment, failed to develop talent.

How Musical Talent Is Produced. The basic equipment must be superiority in the musical aptitudes—the senses of pitch, time, intensity (loudness and softness), harmony, rhythm and musical memory (which can be measured by current standard tests— Seashore, Thorpe-Whistler, Drake, etc.). Degrees of capacity with respect to each of these senses *separately,* and not as a group, appear to be inborn: First, because one sense may be present without the other, so that a person can have a keen sense of time, but not of harmony, or may have a fine sense of rhythm and harmony, but poor musical memory, etc. Second, training cannot be shown to "create" any of these senses, or (say authorities), to improve them much beyond the degree that the inborn capacity for development is there. All this would suggest that there are separate genes for each musical sense, working with different degrees of intensity.

▶ *Absolute pitch.* This is the keenest sense of pitch—the ability to "hit" or judge any note correctly by ear alone. While absolute pitch is found in many virtuosi and is usually revealed in childhood, the great majority of outstanding musicians fail to develop it despite years of practice. On the other hand, many persons without musical training have absolute pitch from the start, and many have it with little else in the way of musical aptitude. Strengthening belief of its inheritance (possibly through a *dominant* gene) is the fact that absolute pitch may run in families for successive generations, as for example in the singer Kirsten Flagstad, her mother, maternal grandmother and maternal granduncle.

▶ *"Tune deafness"* or *"tone deafness."* The inability to carry a tune, or to recognize tunes, which afflicts some individuals, is believed due to heredity in many, if not most cases. In families where it appears there is evidence that the condition may be caused by a dominant gene. If true, such a gene could completely block the appearance of musical aptitude or musical development, regardless of how superior the afflicted person's other musical genes might be.

▶ *"Musicians' hands."* Music experts belittle the popular notion regarding "piano hands" or "violin hands"—that particular shapes of hands or fingers destine a child to become a good musician, and failure to have them means that he won't be. While some hands are unquestionably better constructed than others for developing performing technique, varied types of hands and fingers are found among top musicians, and some have anything but "long, tapering fingers." Any special "sensitivity" in musicians' hands is mostly the result of the way they've been used.

How Musical Virtuosity Might Be Inherited. A good assumption is that although a great many genes contribute to musical talent, the majority are in wide circulation; anyone who can carry a tune or learn to play a musical instrument must have many of them. But the special "key" genes required for great talent are rare. However, the fact that great musical talent can persist through three or four generations would indicate that these "key" genes are limited in number, and are probably *dominant,* since otherwise the needed combination could not long be maintained.

▶ *The "music-gene" theory.* Let us suppose that there are five of the superior or "virtuoso" key genes for the basic musical senses, which we will designate in this way: "M★ U★ S★ I★ C★." Next, the ordinary genes for the same senses could be designated in this way (without the stars): "M–U–S–I–C." Finally, representing the inferior or defective genes (with small letters): "m—u—s—i—c." Since each person receives a pair of genes of every type—one gene from each parent—any combination of superior, ordinary and inferior "talent" genes could be inherited: (M★M—Uu—S★S—I★i—CC), or (Mm—U★U—S★S—II—C★C) or (mm—uu—Ss—II—C★c), etc., producing talent or aptitude in various degrees. Only with at least one virtuoso (starred) gene *of each type* in every pair would great talent result: (M★M—U★U—S★S—I★I—C★C). This could explain a number of hitherto puzzling situations.

▶ *Untalented parents, talented child.* If each parent carried only part of the needed gene-combination, neither parent alone would show much talent. But between them they could contribute all the genes required to produce a highly talented (M★U★-S★I★C★) child.

▶ *Talented parents, untalented children.* Even the most musically talented persons are undoubtedly carrying—in addition to their superior genes—some "hidden" genes which are ordinary and possibly inferior, so it is quite likely that the new gene-combination received by any child will not be as talent-producing as that of the parent. This would be particularly so if the other parent was not talented.

▶ *Talented parents, talented children.* Although an untalented child may also appear, as explained above, the more talent there is in both parents, the greater is the chance that a child will receive the needed "talent-gene" combination. Thus, the author's study of virtuosi musicians and singers showed that where both their parents were talented, there was also talent in about 70 per cent of their brothers and sisters; where one parent was talented, in about 60 per cent; where neither parent was talented, in only 15 per cent.

The Extra "Talent" Requirement. A great deal more than musical aptitude is required if the musician is to reach the heights in his field. Also essential are such qualities as feeling, sensitivity, powers of concentration, drive and stamina, plus "personality." How much heredity may contribute to these qualities is still unknown. At any rate, deficiencies in these traits, as well as unfavorable turns in the environment, may help to explain why so many musical prodigies peter out in later years.

Composing Talent. While the highest degree of musicality is required for the great composer, as for the great musical performer, the special talents needed for one do not necessarily go with those for the other. Many great composers have been undistinguished performers, and many virtuosi musicians have shown no talent for composition. Whatever the special composing gifts may be, they also appear to have an hereditary basis and to reveal themselves through precociousness and spontaneity. Thus Handel was composing church services at eleven; Mozart at fourteen had a score of symphonies and short operas to his credit; and Mendelssohn and Schubert by age seventeen or eighteen were already notable composers. More specific knowledge regarding the role played by heredity in composing talent is lacking mainly because there are as yet no reliable tests for identifying and measuring its basic elements. This is true of all the arts involving "creativity," as we shall explain later.

▶ *Why no women among great composers?* The striking absence of women among the top composers is one of the great mysteries. Many women have shown outstanding talent as musicians, and some have been recognized as among the most gifted composers of songs and études. But no woman has ever been credited with producing a great symphony, or other musical work of the highest type. Possible reasons for this will be discussed toward the end of this chapter.

▶ *"Popular" music.* Virtually all of the musical-talent studies to date have been of musicians in the "classical" field. But there is every possibility that most of the general facts brought out here also apply to outstanding composers and performers of semiclassical and popular music.

VOCAL TALENT. A common mistake is to suppose that to be a great singer, one need only be born with a great voice. But the voice is only an instrument—like the pianist's piano or the violinist's violin. To be an outstanding singer also requires great musical talent, so that the vocal equipment can be developed and used properly. Thus, much of what has been said about the inheritance of musical talent in instrumentalists also applies to singers. The important differences stem from the fact that the singer's instrument is part of himself and that he is at all times at the mercy of its condition. Also, because the permanent quality of the voice cannot be determined until puberty, intensive vocal training usually doesn't begin until then or later. Finally, such external factors as the singer's looks, personality and dramatic ability, plus the whims of the public, play a much greater role in the vocal than in the instrumental fields. Nevertheless, the records of the great singers all point to a high degree of inborn musicality, and their family backgrounds reveal almost as much talent as do those of the virtuosi musicians. (*Note:* For complete details, see the author's "You and Heredity," first edition, 1939, pp. 245-255.)

▶ *Voice types.* Limited evidence of inheritance indicates that *bass* voices in men and *soprano* voices in women are determined by one type of "voice" genes; that a different type of gene produces *tenor* in men, *alto* in women; and that a mixed pair of genes—one of each type—produces *baritone* in men, *mezzo-soprano* in women. The author's own study further suggests that where both parents have high voices (father, tenor; mother, soprano) the children's voices will tend to be in the high range; while baritone or bass fathers tend to produce a marked majority of low-voiced sons. Among European Whites, the highest incidence of bassos and sopranos, 61 per cent, is in northwest Germany, the lowest, 12 per cent, in Sicily.

RACE DIFFERENCES IN MUSICALITY. People of some races or nationalities undoubtedly *show* more talent for music, or for particular forms of musical expression, than do others. One must be struck by the preponderance of Italian opera composers, conductors and singers; of Jewish violinists, pianists and composers of both classical and popular music; of Negroes among jazz musicians, composers and singers; and of the special musical characteristics of various other racial or ethnic groups. Most authorities feel that these can be explained by differences not in heredity, but in musical atmosphere and environment. For example, the psychological environment of Negroes may explain why they express themselves in "blues," in particular types of rhythm, and in their special folk songs and "spirituals"; at the same time with limited chance for training in classical music, their musicians and singers have turned largely to the popular fields. Tests so far made of the basic musical senses of rhythm, time, harmony, etc., have shown no significant differences between Negro and White children, nor of these as compared with other racial and ethnic groups. However, geneticists believe we cannot entirely dismiss the possibility that special types of "music-talent" genes might be distributed differently, to some extent at least, among the peoples of the world. For the time being, it is well to conclude that musical talent is found plentifully among all peoples, and that the degree to which it has expressed itself so far has been largely dependent upon opportunity and training.

ARTS, SCIENCES, CREATIVITY. The talent for music is undoubtedly not alone in requiring special hereditary capacities. Particular inborn endowments may be equally necessary for high achievement in painting, sculpture, writing, acting, dancing and other arts, as well as in science and invention. But in these other fields any inherited factors are harder to identify because of the greater and more complex role played by environment.

▶ *"Born artist."* The term is often rather loosely applied to anyone having characteristics supposed to go with persons engaged in the various arts. It has meaning so far as it relates to individuals with sensitivity, imagination, creativeness and other essentials for artistic achievement. But it is an error to assume that "artistry" is linked with a particular type of face, hair, hand or body. If people who are artistic do show it in any way in their looks, it is only because in the course of time they have developed certain physical traits through their ways of working, thinking and living. In the cases of any child, however, there is no way one can tell from his physical characteristics that he is or isn't a "born" artist.

▶ *Elements of artistry.* In all the arts the basic components are much the same: The feeling for composition, form, rhythm, shadings of expression (nuances), and the more elusive aforementioned qualities of "creativeness," "sensitiveness" and "imagination." It is not improbable that these elements are much influenced by some general hereditary endowment, which may explain why artistic or creative persons usually show talents of various kinds, and often excel in several fields simultaneously.

But proficiency in a specific art demands additional special abilities, and therefore special supplementary genes (as we have already seen in the case of music). The great painter must have a keen eye for color, which would rule out the color-blind person (although he would not be prevented, if he had great artistic ability, from being an etcher or sculptor). So, too, great fiction-writing, drama, poetry or other arts, undoubtedly demand special sensory and personality factors, all of which may be conditioned by heredity as well as environment. Thus, a general "artistic heredity," plus an "artistic environment," may explain families in which many members for successive generations were outstanding in one or another of the arts. At the same time, added specific requirements may explain why some members excelled in one art form, some in another form, and some (lacking necessary "key" genes) showed talent in none of the arts.

GENIUS. The clearest indications that great talents are inborn come from studying the backgrounds and histories of true "geniuses": the rare individuals, arising once or twice in a century, who reach the topmost levels of human achievement. Socrates, Leonardo da Vinci, Michelangelo, Shakespeare, Newton, Beethoven, Franklin, Lincoln, Edison, Einstein—these have been among them. In former times geniuses were awesomely regarded as products of supernatural and mysterious forces. Today science sees the genius as someone initially endowed with a *rare and unusual combination of superior genes.* Obviously, environment also plays a part in permitting the seeds of genius to take root and flourish. But the belief that geniuses are the products primarily of unusual heredity rests on the fact that no special type of environment can be shown to have produced them, and that geniuses have arisen in many types of environment.

▶ *Leonardo and Shakespeare.* Perhaps the most amazing genius of all time was Leonardo da Vinci. The illegitimate son of a Florentine peasant girl and a minor official of the fifteenth century, Leonardo as a child spontaneously displayed a bewildering variety of talents. These he proceeded to develop—many of them without training or precedent—until eventually he led his world in sculpture, painting, science, mathematics, engineering and invention, and was also notable as a musician and a poet. There seems to be no other explanation for Leonardo except phenomenal inborn endowment. Nor can any environment explain the incredible literary and dramatic powers of Shakespeare, who, too, came from an obscure background, with little schooling and nothing exceptional in the way of opportunity.

▶ *The "genius" genes.* Having already dealt with various "talent" genes, we may now seek the answer to genius in the most potent and rarest of the human "achievement" genes which make possible the maximum development of human senses and mental powers. Most persons would probably not be carrying any of these genes, some persons might carry one or two; but only once in many millions of times would a couple in any generation be carrying between them all of the genes required to produce a genius. The parents themselves, each lacking some of the essential "genius" genes, might be nobodies—which explains why geniuses so often seem to arise suddenly out of nowhere. Again, the chance that a child of a genius would receive exactly the same, or an equally remarkable combination of genes, is exceedingly remote, which could explain why successive geniuses do not follow in the same family. (Illustration, p. 171.)

▶ *Are geniuses "abnormal"?* There is a long-standing belief that geniuses must be mentally or physically abnormal in some way. To back this up, lists have been compiled of geniuses and near-geniuses who suffered from various mental or physical disorders: Socrates, Molière, Nietzsche, Caesar, Napoleon, Van Gogh, etc. On the other hand, it has been pointed out that many other persons of genius caliber were fully normal in every ordinary sense. As examples, of men close to our own time, and of whom we can speak with accuracy: Benjamin Franklin, Thomas Jefferson, Lincoln, Shaw, Churchill, Einstein. It remains possible that the incidence of physical and mental abnormalities may have been, and may now be, higher than average among geniuses and other highly creative persons, not because abnormality goes with their "genius" genes, but for these reasons: 1) A person with unusual talent, who is not physically or mentally average or "normal," may be especially likely to think in unconventional ways and do unusual things; 2) talented persons who are maladjusted, sickly or otherwise "different," may have an exceptional drive to "compensate" by working feverishly toward their goals; 3) persons far in advance of their times in their thinking or creations are likely to be considered "queer" by their contemporaries, and if this leads to added social and financial stresses, they may have an above-average chance of cracking up. Today the better understanding of the nature of genius and improved methods of educating and rearing exceptionally talented children may very well diminish such relationship as there has been between genius and "queerness."

▶ *Longevity of geniuses.* Another popular belief, that geniuses tend to be short-lived, is not supported by evidence. Many geniuses in the past did die young, but this was when average life spans were short. On the other hand, many geniuses lived to very ripe old ages: Michelangelo, Titian, Rubens, Newton, Shaw, Sibelius, Matisse, Rouault. A recent analysis shows that the average longevity of thousands of geniuses and near-geniuses was no less than that of their respective generations.

PRODIGIES. While most geniuses were prodigies—children with exceptional mental powers or talents—it does not follow that every prodigy is a potential genius. Some prodigies may be "incomplete" geniuses, endowed with only some of the required "genius" genes (or with other mental stimuli) which may start them off in a remarkable way but not carry them too far. In other cases a prodigy is equipped with only a phenomenal memory, or quick reading and learning ability, which enables him to go through school studies by leaps and bounds. In still other cases clever and ambitious parents may succeed, by intensive training, to induce precociousness in a child. But whenever a child's reasoning ability or innate talents are also not exceptional, as is very often the case, a letdown in achievement generally results at maturity. Parents and teachers should therefore be extremely cautious about overestimating the importance of seemingly precocious mental powers or other gifts in children, and trying to force their development.

▶ *Mathematical prodigies.* As with musical genius (to which it appears to be related in some ways), phenomenal mathematical ability usually appears spontaneously at very early ages, many of the greatest mathematicians—Galois and Leibnitz, and among contemporaries, Norbert Wiener and Julian Schwinger— having been prodigies. Further, while great mathematical achievement requires great intellect, mathematical aptitude of itself (again as with musical aptitude) need not be related to intelligence. Many phenomenal mental calculators had or have mediocre minds in all other respects, and some have been found

How Genius Is Produced

"Genius" genes: ☆ ☆   Ordinary genes: O O

FATHER

Average, but carries some hidden "genius" genes.

MOTHER

Average, but carries other needed "genius" genes.

All the needed "genius" genes are combined in the **CHILD.**

With the required environment, a *genius* results.

Environment

GENIUS

becomes adult

WIFE

average, with mostly ordinary genes.

CHILD receives only part of the needed "genius" genes.

Grows up to be ordinary.

among the feeble-minded, these being known as *"idiot savants."* Because unusual mathematical ability has been found running in families for as many as five generations, some authorities believe it may be produced by a single *dominant* (or Dom.-Q.) gene.

▶ *Chess talent.* Chess-playing ability appears to be a specialized offshoot of mathematical ability, in which the traits of phenomenal memory and of visualizing complicated arrangements are principal factors. Some hereditary basis is also indicated. Thus, as with both musical and mathematical aptitude, phenomenal chess-playing aptitude appears in childhood, almost every chess master on record having been a child prodigy in the field. (The top-ranking chess player of the United States, Samuel Reshevsky, was giving chess-playing exhibitions at the age of six.)

SEX DIFFERENCES IN ACHIEVEMENT. Earlier in this chapter we touched upon the puzzling absence of women among the great composers. Equally puzzling is the fact that while women are among the fine painters and sculptors, none has achieved ranking with the very best, that is of the caliber of the top old-masters, or of Cézanne, Picasso, Matisse, Jacob Epstein, etc. In literature, poetry and drama, despite the many women who have made outstanding contributions, it can hardly be said that any have approached the status of Shakespeare, Molière or Shaw. Nor in science, with full recognition of the achievements of Mme. Curie, Lisa Meitner and several others, have there as yet been any women Newtons or Einsteins. As for *inventors,* one finds virtually no women among them. How explain this? It has been argued that the reasons are entirely environmental: That women in the past never had equal opportunity to develop in the creative fields, and that even today a great many more disadvantages and inhibitions may exist for women of talent than for men.

▶ *The genetic argument.* Allowing for all adverse environmental factors, the possibility remains that inherent differences between the sexes might affect the ways in which talents can be expressed and developed in them. We have seen that the same genes for many physical traits—body form, stature, disease, etc.

—may work quite differently in the two sexes and produce different results. With the same "stature" genes a brother will grow to be several inches taller than a sister; with the same "muscle" genes he will become very much stronger. Might this possibly be true of the genes for various talents? Or at least, might not the achievement *trends* of women be inherently different from those of men? There is little evidence on this point, except as offered by aptitude tests of little boys and girls before their environments have become too different. These tests (discussed in Chapter 19) show little girls to be superior in learning to speak, read and acquire vocabularies, in noticing details, and in sensing people's reactions. Could this explain why among all the arts, women are relatively best in fiction and poetry? Little boys show superiority in mathematical, structural, and abstract reasoning tests. Since such aptitudes are highly important in musical composition, painting, sculpture and drama, as well as in science and invention, could this not help to explain male preeminence in these fields?

▶ *Conclusions.* Whatever the present arguments or limited facts, it is not likely that with women constituted differently from men by inborn factors, and with the probability that they will also continue to be reared, trained and employed differently in many ways, we will ever have complete answers as to what their relative abilities may be. A guess that might be made is that women's drives and capacities are not the same as men's, and that they therefore have been at a disadvantage in following male formulas and methods, and trying to compete with men in precisely the same types of achievement. Perhaps as women express *themselves* more, and have increased opportunities to develop such special gifts as they may have, their creative achievements will become ever greater. For the present it is already evident that growing numbers of women are forging ahead in all creative fields, with many of them excelling a large proportion of the men in the same fields. (For further facts on *sex differences in achievement,* see the author's book, "Women and Men," Chapters 8, 22, 23, 24, 25.)

21

Behavior

BEHAVIOR DIFFERENCES. The most important thing about human individuals in relation to one another is how they *behave*. Is a person pleasant or unpleasant? Calm or hot-tempered? Kind or cruel? Decent or viciously criminal? Lazy or enterprising? Timid or aggressive? And so on. We have seen that heredity governs people's looks, and to a great extent their body-functioning and intelligence. Does heredity also destine or incline individuals to behave in specific ways? An immediate difficulty in answering is that we know human behavior differs greatly in different environments, and that even the behavior of the same person varies considerably at different stages of life and under different conditions. Nevertheless, as we shall see, beneath the layer of outside influences there quite probably are differences in people's behavior "machinery" which may strongly affect their acts, personalities and reactions to others.

"Instincts." If there are any inherited behavior tendencies in human beings, these must be similar to what we call "instincts" in lower animals. "Instinct" refers to an *inborn* tendency to do things or behave in certain ways without training. Some psychologists dislike using the term on the ground that the behavior of lower animals even in a natural state may be considerably influenced by experience, learning from their elders and changes in environment. In place of "instincts," terms such as "conditioned reflexes," "stimuli," "drives," etc., are suggested. But this may be quibbling. For most authorities, and for the general reader, it is clear that each species throughout its long history had and has its own spontaneous (unlearned) ways of courting and mating, building nests or shelters, seeking and selecting food, caring for young, getting along with its own kind, reacting to enemies, etc. Whether we think of bees, beavers, bears, bunnies, bulls, bullfinches, bluefish, boas, baboons, billy goats or butterflies, we can identify with each species particular types of *inborn* behavior which are almost as much a part of them as are the shapes of their heads and bodies.

Are there "human" instincts? People constantly speak of their "instincts": "He has the 'right' instinct"; "Her instinct told her," "They instinctively liked each other," etc. And, in a general way, we refer to "human" or "inhuman instincts." In the earliest stages of mankind the behavior of humans undoubtedly was governed by as many, if not more instincts, as those in lower animals. We can be sure that humans, too, started off with inborn behavior patterns which directed their mating, caring for their young, selecting and securing food, fighting or avoiding enemies, etc. Otherwise they could not have gone far on the road to survival. Any genes governing such instincts which human beings had we probably still have in great measure today. But the biggest difference between human beings and lower animals is that, going with our superior brains, we also have the capacity to control, modify and train our instincts, and at the same time to change and improve our environments so that the need for our instincts would be lessened. Thus, as civilization has progressed and as life and training have become increasingly complex, the human instincts have been pushed further into the background as only *starting points* for behavior.

▶ *Dependency period.* Aiding the environmental influences on human behavior is the fact that the period of dependency—before offspring become mature and can lead their own lives—is greater for humans than for other animals, giving parents much more opportunity to train their children. Among apes, however, the period of "childhood" is almost as great (chimpanzees and gorillas not reaching puberty until the age of about nine or ten). So for the most part, it is still the inherited flexibility of the human mind and its capacity for being molded that permits training and experience to greatly influence our behavior.

▶ *Infant behavior.* Evidence that the "instinct" genes have not been bred out of us can be seen when we watch infants. As babies come into the world, inborn tendencies to behave in definite ways show themselves in the way they feed, move, grab, smile, etc. Moreover, there seems to be an inherited "time-clock" mechanism which sets off given types of behavior at given stages: When the baby will first begin to bubble, coo; turn over, sit up; observe and grab things; walk; respond to language, talk, be ready for toilet training, etc. This behavior is common to babies among all peoples, civilized and primitive. It is taken so much for granted that when babies anywhere fail to react in the expected ways at the appropriate stages, parents rightfully worry. At the same time, it is also expected and noted that (within the prescribed limits) particular babies will behave in particular ways. In fact, any two babies of the same mother are apt to be no more alike in what they do and when they do it than in their looks. But we know that the individual behavior patterns of infants are much more conditioned than are their looks by their experiences in the womb, and by many subtle in-fluences after they are born. So we can be far less sure of the part that heredity may play in producing these individual dif-ferences than of its effects either on infants' looks or on their general patterns of behavior. (Further discussion in chapter fol-lowing under "Infant personality.")

SOCIAL INSTINCTS. As in infancy, so in later ages and among peoples of all kinds, we can see certain similar patterns of behavior: Mothers nursing and fondling their young; little males wrestling or fighting older males; youths or adult males strutting or performing to impress females, and females acting coyly, flirtatiously or enticingly; two males violently aroused and battling over a female; groups of individuals trustingly fol-lowing a dominant leader, etc. All such behavior is paralleled in lower animals. More important, various scientific studies and experiments have linked this, and other kinds of behavior in lower animals, with biological factors often found to be hered-itary. Animals have been bred in which one or another of these "social" traits is expressed in greater or lesser degree. Also, marked changes in such types of behavior can be produced in individual animals by causing an increase or decrease in the production of certain hormones, or by operating on certain brain and nerve centers. How far this applies to human beings is uncertain, but here are some interesting findings:

▶ *Parental behavior.* As is well known, many different forms and degrees of parental instincts appear among lower animals. In humans we also speak of "natural-born" mothers or fathers; or "motherly" or "fatherly" types, and their opposites. But while in lower animals it is clear that parental behavior is largely governed by hormonal stimuli and other biological factors, among human beings individual differences in this respect appear to be conditioned mainly by social and psychological influences. However, some authorities report that degrees of "motherliness" among women tend to go with certain physical factors which show themselves in breast types, hip forms, menstrual functioning, etc., as well as with certain types of behavior recognizable even in young girls.

▶ *"Dominance."* Are some human beings born to be "bossed" and others to be leaders (irrespective of intelligence)? Among various animal species it has been found that individuals in any group can be graded according to degrees of "dominance" or "submissiveness." In most flocks of birds or poultry a "peck order" can be observed: A given bird pecks at another which submits, but which in turn can peck submissive birds lower in the scale. In groups of apes, mice and perhaps even dogs (according to a recent study) similar rankings of dominance and submissiveness may be found. Also proved or indicated is that when the hormonal makeup of the individual is changed by treatment or operation, his or her standing in the "dominance order" also changes. It may be guessed that in human beings, too, hormonal states—inborn or otherwise—influence the dominance feelings and behavior of individuals towards others. But how far the biology, rather than the psychology, of persons, is involved in most of their relationships, remains to be established.

▶ *"Aggressiveness."* As with "dominance," degrees of aggressiveness or lack of it have been found conditioned in lower animals by their hormonal workings and brain functioning, differences in which can be hereditary. In human individuals, also, varying internal states contribute to their feeling "high" or "low," pugnacious or docile, on occasions. But again, since psychological factors can produce the same results, it may be very difficult in any given cases to show that these traits in persons have an hereditary basis.

▶ *"Fear."* Tendencies to special types of fears are inherited by each lower animal species, and help to protect them against their natural enemies or hazards. One can only assume that buried deep in the human "unconscious" there also are inherited fear tendencies which aided our remote ancestors. But in modern individuals most fears have been shown by psychologists to be conditioned by personal experiences, often in the earliest years. Even women's fears of mice or snakes, which were once considered "instinctive," appear to be mostly psychological and easily overcome by training, as is proved in many college laboratories where girl students work unconcernedly with these animals.

SENSORY REACTIONS. The responses of persons to tastes, smells, sounds, pain and color, affect their everyday behavior and social relationships in many ways, and for this reason are extensively studied by psychologists. That heredity plays an important part in sensory reactions is obvious, most clearly so in the case of the lower animals, each species of which is characterized by its own special sensory equipment. Among human beings, inheritance of individual sensory differences has so far been established mainly with respect to abnormalities or defects in color vision, smell and taste (Chapter 14), and in the musical senses, including tune deafness (Chapter 20). Otherwise, while a considerable range of difference is apparent among individuals in sensitivity to foods, perfumes and odors, pain, noise, drugs, etc., the role of heredity with respect to these differences remains to be clarified. Such investigation is not easy, because of the fact that the development of the human senses in given directions—as in the preferences for or aversions to given foods, odors or colors—and the degrees to which tastes express themselves, are much influenced by training and individual psychological factors.

22

Personality and
Temperament

WHAT "PERSONALITY" MEANS. First, it refers to all of a human individual's behavior traits (discussed in the last chapter), *plus* all the other special qualities of mind, body, sex, and social adjustment that distinguish him as a particular *person.* Second, personality refers to qualities developed by one person in relation to other persons. Strictly speaking, then, only human beings can be considered as having "personalities." Although we might like to think that cats, dogs and other animals also have "personalities," scientists prefer to speak of their traits as "behavior patterns." A distinction is that behavior traits are simpler, and as we have seen, can be almost directly inherited in lower animals in the form of "instincts." It is far less certain whether any personality traits are ever directly inherited.

▶ *Infant personality.* Human infants, like other little animals, come into the world with inherited behavior patterns, as noted in the last chapter. But from the moment they begin to be trained and influenced by their parents, older children, nurses and other human beings, they cease to be merely instinctive creatures, and any inborn tendencies become only the raw materials from which the forces outside of them mold their personalities. How far the inherited tendencies can push their way through the conditioning forces, and stay on top, is a question. Some studies (Dr. M. M. Shirley, Dr. Patricia Neilon) which have followed the same individuals from infancy through adolescence, indicate that in most cases those who were especially good-natured, alert, aggressive, difficult, etc. (or the opposite), tended to have the same personality traits in later years. Many mothers will confirm this in their children. But theories that children's personalities are greatly affected by whether they were breast fed or bottle fed, weaned early or late, diaper

179

trained one way or another, continue to be debated, without conclusive findings.

Physical Influences. In addition to the obvious mental and nervous disorders, a great many inherited diseases, defects and organic weaknesses or peculiarities have characteristic effects on personality. Persons suffering from migraine headaches, for example, have been reported as tending to show "intolerance, perfectionism, sexual difficulties, etc." Particular personality patterns may also go with glandular disorders, allergies, vitamin deficiencies, digestive disturbances and other conditions in which heredity may play a part. Changes in the body's chemical state or functioning by means of various drugs, and operations on the brain and nervous system, have been shown to affect personality in many ways. One may assume, then, that any inherited differences—large or small—in the workings of the glands and other organs would account for some degree of difference in the personalities of individuals. The body's chemical transitions at adolescence, during the menopause in women, and in aging, also have their definite effects on personality. But very probably, beneath the outer personality layers of individuals which can be much affected by changes in health or other factors, there is always an *inner core* of personality which persists through life. And it is this "inner personality" which may be strongly directed by inherited tendencies.

LOOKS AND PERSONALITY. People have always believed that certain looks go with certain personalities. From Shakespeare's plays through to modern novels, dramas, movies, comic strips and TV shows, one will find people with given types of faces and bodies cast as characters with given personality traits: Heroines, fair, slim and lovely. Heroes, tall, straight and handsome. Villains, lean and swarthy. Redheads, fiery natures. Bold men depicted with jutting jaws, weaklings with receding chins, sneaky people with warped bodies, etc. Science has found no such connection between genes for looks and genes for personality, character or temperament. The only exceptions are in certain inherited diseases and abnormal conditions (discussed in earlier chapters) which may together affect both outward appearance and behavior. Otherwise almost any kind of nose, eyes,

Looks and Personality

All of these notions are wrong!

  CHINS **BROWS**

RECEDING:	**PROTRUDING:**	**LOW:**	**HIGH:**
"Weakness"	"Bravery"	"Low IQ"	"High IQ"
"Timidity"	"Determination"	"Brutality"	"Loftiness"

  NOSE **NOSE**

UPTILTED:	**ROUND:**	**SHARP, THIN:**	**LARGE:**
"Pertness"	"Geniality"	"Meanness"	"Virility"
"Impulsiveness"	"Softness"	"Cruelty"	"Aggression"

  EYES **MOUTH**

CLOSE-TOGETHER, SMALL:	**WIDE-APART, LARGE:**	**SMALL, THIN:**	**LARGE, WIDE:**
"Meanness"	"Frankness"	"Coldness"	"Sensuousness"
"Foxiness"	"Honesty"	"Selfishness"	"Generosity"
"Slyness"	"Sincerity"		

   EARS **HAIR**

SMALL:	**LARGE:**	**STRAIGHT:**	**CURLY:**
"Refinement"	"Commonness"	"Seriousness"	"Frivolity"
"Sensitivity"	"Stupidity"	"Placidity"	"Artistry"
	(if protruding)		

The genes that determine physical traits need not at all be related to the genes that affect personality traits. (See text.)

mouth, complexion, coloring or other bodily detail can go with any kind of inborn personality tendency. However, *facial expressions* involve something else. The way a person has used and uses his mouth and eyes may offer real clues to his personality, as may also movements of the head, body, hands, etc.

▶ *Body build* (*somatotypes*). In recent years the theory has been revived that given types of body build do in a general way go with given types of personality and temperament, presumably because the same glandular and other factors which affect body build also may produce certain behavior tendencies. (This would in turn bring heredity into the picture so far as it governs these glandular and other workings.) One of the first to claim this relationship was Dr. E. Kretschmer, who classified people as "pyknic" (fat), "aesthenic" (lean), and "athletic" types, ascribing certain general personality characteristics to each. More recently Dr. W. H. Sheldon has devised these classifications: *Endomorphs* (soft, round physiques, tending to obesity)—"inclined to be home-loving, placid, sociable"; *Mesomorphs* (athletic, muscular, heavy-boned)—"likely to be fighters, leaders, heroes, lovers of thrills and action"; *Ectomorphs* (slim, flat-chested, stringy-muscled)—"inclined to be 'mental' and alert, but not too aggressive, forward or at ease with people." Various gradations and in-between types of physiques are rated by how much of each "morph" component there is in an individual's body build. Many psychiatrists consider these classifications helpful in diagnoses (if used with other evidence). But authorities differ as to their dependability, and especially, as to whether they can be related to *inherited* personality traits. (See also Chap. 23, "somatotypes of juvenile delinquents.")

▶ *"Physiognomy" and "phrenology."* Still persisting and taken seriously are old notions, that different "areas" or parts of the face and head are in some way tied up with specific mental traits, and therefore can reveal character. For instance, that "development of various areas of the nose reflect capacity for observation, imagination, etc."; or that in the areas of the temple and eyebrows one can read such and such other traits. To this, as to "phrenology," which purports to read character through bumps on the head, reputable scientists say, simply: *"Bunk."*

Effects of Looks. While heredity may couple any kind of feature or looks with any kind of personality trait, people themselves tend to ignore this fact. As a result, personalities can be much affected by how looks are regarded. If a little girl is drooled over because she's "so pretty," she certainly won't develop the same personality as will a homely sister. Similarly, to the extent that people react differently to tall or short persons, slender or fat ones, blondes and brunettes, the fair-skinned or dark-skinned, or to this or that kind of mouth or nose, the individuals' personalities will also develop differently. But it is important to remember: Attitudes toward the very same types of looks—nose size, hip size, leg shape, skin color—may differ greatly in different groups, and when they do, so do the effects on personalities. Fat women in the United States are made to feel inferior, and slim women feel superior; but in some parts of the Orient and Africa the plumpest women are the glamour girls, and the slim ones are the wallflowers. A few decades ago girls with small bosoms were most approved among Americans (as they still are among Japanese), and those with large bosoms self-consciously tried to strap them down. As need hardly be said, there's been a change. So, too, the small, cupid's-bow mouth has currently yielded in desirability to the full, large mouth; and increases in stature have revised the scale by which persons are rated and feel themselves "too tall" or "too short." The genes for looks remain the same generation after generation, but their effects on personalities may be almost anything that people wish to make them.

HANDS, FEET, ANKLES. The notion that thick, large hands and ankles betoken peasant or common ancestry, and a coarse personality, whereas slim hands and ankles go with "aristocratic" or genteel ancestry and inherent refinement, has no scientific support. It is true that people who do heavy manual work in time develop thicker hands and ankles than those who do not, but these effects cannot be passed on through inheritance; and if the descendants themselves no longer do heavy work, they may have just as slim hands or ankles as those of "aristocratic" blood. Apart from the direct effects of work and living habits, the sizes, shapes or textures of hands and feet have no relationship to personality factors. (For "Musicians' hands," see Chap. 20.)

▶ *"Palmistry."* Despite claims of "palmists" and their writings (and the enormous number of people who believe them), science has found absolutely no relationship between specific lines in palms and any inborn traits of personality, mental qualities, success tendencies, or what not. Even more, the belief that anyone can predict future events (whom one will marry, how long one will live, or how many children one will have) by "reading" palm lines is pure superstition. Clever palmists may sometimes make good guesses, but only as any keen observer might do, not by looking at the palms but by noting details of a person's general appearance, behavior and speech.

Mannerisms. Characteristic movements of the mouth, eyes, hands and head, or ways of walking, praying, etc., observed in groups of people from the same stocks, countries or localities, almost invariably result from formed habits, and are no more hereditary than are their languages or accents. Likewise, those in given occupations (farmers, policemen, sailors, actresses, etc.) develop distinctive ways of gesturing and moving. Children, in turn, tend consciously or unconsciously to imitate their parents, so it is not surprising to find certain mannerisms running in families. However, there are cases where some odd or unusual gesture or movement of a parent seems to appear spontaneously in a child (as in a son who has never seen his father). This leaves open the possibility that such mannerisms may arise through inherited muscular reflexes. Adding to the theory are findings at Jackson Memorial Laboratory that different breeds of dogs have their characteristic involuntary movements.

"Astrology." This is mentioned here only because so many millions of people who read "astrology" books and consult "astrologers" or "astrological horoscopes" sincerely believe that their personalities were and are dictated, and their fortunes governed by, the stars they were "born under." It may shock or anger them to be told that true scientists regard "astrology" as no science at all, but, like "palmistry," as mere superstition. Incidentally, one should not confuse "astrology" with "astronomy" (although in ancient times the two were linked). Astronomy is now the recognized science that deals with the stars and planets, and their movements. But astronomers reject all the hocus-pocus going with "astrology," and some years ago one of their official committees (headed by Harvard professor Bart J. Bok) flatly stated that "astrology is a magical practice which has no shred of justification in fact." Note, for example, that among twins (discussed next) the fact that they were "born under the same star" by no means makes their personalities or fortunes the same—particularly if they are fraternal twins who may be as different in personality as any two children of a family born under different stars.

TWIN STUDIES. While difficult, if not impossible, to prove inheritance of personality as a whole, significant evidence has come through analyses of separate traits as shown by identical and fraternal twins. In major respects many personality traits of identical twins are usually much alike, whereas those of fraternal twins are not. It is true that identical twins are reared more closely together. However, remarkable similarities in traits have also developed in identical twins separated in early infancy and reared widely apart in different localities and types of homes.

▶ *Specific findings.* Two studies reported in 1955 tend to strengthen the personality-inheritance theory. One, by Drs. Raymond B. Cattell, Duncan B. Blewett and John R. Beloff, involved comparisons of personality traits of almost a thousand individuals, among them scores of identical and fraternal twin pairs, and of non-twin members of many families. The findings led to these conclusions: Heredity may play a leading role in making some persons more easygoing, sociable and warmhearted, or bolder and more outgoing, than others. But environment predominates in producing a "happy-go-lucky" nature and impulsiveness. In another study, Dr. Steven G. Vandenberg compared personality traits of forty-five pairs of identical and thirty-seven of fraternal twins (all high-school students). He found so much more similarity between the identicals in likes and dislikes for music, art, clothes and color, and in degrees of self-confidence and stubbornness, as to conclude that heredity must be strongly involved in producing these traits.

▶ *The Dionne quintuplets.* Personality studies of this famous set (discussed in Chapter 5) were made only in their early years. Certain differences in their personalities were observed, but these were for the most part no greater than those which parents recognize between any two identical twins. However, limited recent information has indicated that some of the initial differences persisted and became strongly marked in the later ages, particularly with respect to Marie, and to the late Emilie (who died in 1954). As noted in Chapter 5, these two were almost like a pair of twins within the set of five, probably having been the last to develop from the same final subdivision of the egg. Marie was the weakest, sickliest and shyest, while Emilie was epileptic, and both were less poised and less well adjusted than the other three. The two, also, had entered convents, then given up the plan to become nuns. At this writing Marie is uncertain about her future; Yvonne and Cecile are training to be nurses; and Annette is studying music.

GENERAL CONCLUSIONS. The divergence among the Dionnes—despite their all having exactly the same hereditary factors—is only a partial indication of how far any inherited personality tendencies may be influenced by environment. At the same time, their personality differences have been and are probably much less than their similarities, as compared with any equal group of girls taken at random, or even any four or five separately born sisters reared in the same way. Altogether, the facts about the Dionnes, and other findings discussed in this and preceding chapters, warrant only these conclusions: There undoubtedly are genes which incline individuals to develop personalities in given directions, and different from those of other individuals, when environmental factors are the same. Any such "personality" genes, however, are far less direct, definite or forceful in their workings, and much more likely to be swerved off course, than are the genes for the physical traits or mental capacities. In sum, heredity provides only the raw materials for personality development. But these same raw materials in any person can be processed, shaped and packaged in a great many different ways.

See also: *Sex differences in personality:* Chap. 24. *Race differences in personality:* Chap. 27. *Abnormal (psychopathic) personality:* Chap. 16. *Criminal personality:* Chap. 23.

23

Criminal Behavior

"**CRIMINAL TAINTS.**" It is an old belief that "evil streaks" or "criminal taints" run in certain families, and also, that some human groups, nationalities or races are more "criminal" by nature than others. No scientific evidence for this has yet been produced. Further, there are only guesses or suppositions about the extent to which individuals in any group may inherit tendencies toward criminality. On the other hand, we can now refute or question many of the earlier theories about criminal inheritance. It is these *disproofs* regarding criminality that are perhaps most important.

▶ *What is the "criminal type"?* Our first difficulty in trying to find out whether criminality is inborn is to decide what we mean by it. Legal and social definitions of "criminality" vary and have varied enormously, depending on places or periods. Nor can we distinguish between "criminals" and "non-criminals" merely on the basis of those who have or haven't been convicted of wrongdoing, since law and justice are far from always the same. But even when a person's acts are so consistently vicious and antisocial as to clearly stamp him a criminal, we still have to dig deeply into his background, makeup and thinking before we can assume that his heredity may be in any way responsible. Finally, the many types of crime—murder, robbery, rape, drug addiction, tax evasion, fraud, etc.—may often be completely unrelated; and even the same crimes (as murders, or sex offenses) may be of many different types in nature and motive. To find genes causing "criminality" in general might be as impossible as to find genes for "disease" in general. Only when we examine separately each form of crime and those committing it can we begin to see what causative forces might be at work.

HEREDITARY FACTORS IN CRIME. Keeping in mind the foregoing reservations, there is nevertheless some basis for believing that certain persons might be especially predisposed to commit crimes of various kinds, or of specific kinds, because of inborn quirks. The evidence to support this, however, is only circumstantial or inferential.

▶ *Crime in twins.* Studies of crime among twins have shown that where they were identicals (with the same hereditary factors), if one was criminal, so was the other in at least four out of five cases, whereas in fraternal twins (with different heredity) this was true in only about one in three. But when weighing this evidence one must remember that identical twins are usually reared more closely together, and one influences the other more than is true of fraternal twins.

▶ *Mental disease and crime.* Where acts of violence or other crimes arise through mental diseases, such as schizophrenia, manic-depressive insanity, or psychopathic personality, heredity obviously is involved to the extent that it plays a part in these diseases. (Chap. 16.) There is also limited recent evidence that a disproportionate number of criminals have abnormal brain-wave patterns, the findings being clearest in the cases of those who have committed murders, violence or acts of cruelty on sudden impulses and without rational motivation. However, the majority of criminals show no symptoms of diseased minds, and appear to be no more than warped products of unfortunate conditioning, experiences and circumstances.

▶ *Feeble-mindedness and crime.* Authorities are also finding less and less connection between low intelligence and crime. A generation ago about 35 per cent of the prison inmates were feeble-minded and (as with insanity), where heredity could be blamed for the mental defect, it might also be blamed for the criminal acts. Today, with better care and training, and more good institutional homes, fewer of the mentally retarded get into trouble or reach prisons. As a result, Dr. David Wechsler, IQ expert, tells us that the IQs of present-day prison inmates are close to the general average, with many (particularly forgers and "white-collar" offenders) being of high intelligence. In some places average IQs of prison inmates may continue to be low if the least intelligent are the ones most likely to be arrested and convicted, as was commonly true in the past.

▶ *Chemical factors in crime.* Recent studies point to deviations from the average in the body chemistry of criminals as a group, leading some authorities to believe that chemical factors may be an unbalancing influence and a motivating force toward certain types of antisocial or criminal acts. Among such factors cited are sugar deficiency in the blood (*hypoglycemia*), which may impair sensory reactions and judgments, and increase aggressiveness; calcium deficiency, making persons extremely sensitive and quick to violence; and various glandular disorders which affect the brain and behavior of persons.

▶ *Criminal "looks" and "somatotypes."* "Findings" have been reported from time to time that criminals as a group differ from non-criminals in features or body build. But as was stated in Chapter 22, there is no evidence that any inherited facial or bodily detail goes with any particular behavior trait (other than in rare cases where defective genes produce both physical and mental abnormalities). Thus, most authorities have viewed skeptically successive theories (Lombroso, Hooton, etc.) that persons committing crimes of given kinds tend to have such and such ears, eyes, foreheads, mouths, chins or noses. Where there is any recognizable "criminal" look, it is perhaps only because of the person's expressions and the "set" of the face, resulting from habits. Most recently there have been the "body-build" theories—that criminals, or juvenile delinquents, tend to have characteristic "somatotypes" (types of bodies). This has also been questioned, although it is possible that since some types of crime tend to be committed more often in some groups than other groups, any differences among these groups in body build would be reflected in the criminal population.

ENVIRONMENT AND CRIME. Whatever part heredity may play in crime is greatly overshadowed by the effects of environment. This is clearly proved by the enormous differences in the rates of crime among people of the same stock, from one generation to the next, or in one locality as compared with another, as their conditions, training and attitudes change. A striking example is the *murder* rate. Among Americans, murders were for decades far more common than among their European relatives with the same heredity. This included the Germans, who were long regarded as among the most civilized, law-abiding and disciplined of peoples. But during the mad period of Nazi rule, the murders and vicious crimes of every kind in Germany reached staggering totals. Nor is there doubt that if Americans or other people were engulfed by the same kind of psychological madness, crime would be equally rampant among them. Again, looking within the United States itself, we find tremendous differences in the murder and crime rates of different regions, states and cities, and in neighborhoods of the same city, even though the people may all be of similar hereditary makeup. As a general rule, regardless of people's heredity, crime rates are highest wherever social and psychological conditions are worst, the government and police most corrupt and inefficient, and the public most tolerant toward wrongdoing.

▶ *Juvenile delinquency.* Drastic increases in crimes and lawlessness among young people in the United States and other countries during and since World War II are further proof of environmental influences. Formerly the chief causes of delinquency were considered to be poverty, bad social conditions, broken homes, etc. More recently, since delinquency has also mounted among children from the most privileged and educated groups, attention is turning as well to psychological and emotional factors, inside and outside the homes. However, the fact that under any given condition only some young people become delinquent and most others do not, and some commit horrible crimes difficult to explain, raises the possibility of inborn tendencies or predispositions in many instances. Moreover, as noted in a preceding section, *"What is the 'criminal type'?"* one must distinguish between different types of delinquency. Those involving sex offenses, or theft, or drug addiction, or assaults, or vicious behavior, may be quite unrelated, and in some the possibility of hereditary tendencies may be greater than in others. There is much in this area that scientists need to explore before definite answers can be given.

Racial and ethnic differences in crime. While rates for crime as a whole, and for specific crimes, vary greatly among persons of different foreign stocks and races in the United States, this, too, may well be traced to the different conditions under which they have been reared, their traditions, occupations and habits. There are times when persons may feel ashamed or disturbed because given types of crime seem unduly prevalent among individuals of their own race, religion or ethnic group. But this may have no more to do with their genes than corned beef and cabbage has to do with Irish genes, sauerbraten with German genes, kosher salami with Jewish genes, spaghetti with Italian genes, etc. Thus, crime differences among Americans of all origins have tended to diminish or disappear as their ways of living and habits have become the same. ("Racial 'Stereotypes,'" Chap. 27.)

▶ *Negro-White crime differences*. The higher *recorded* crime rate of American Negroes as compared with Whites also has nothing to do with inherent differences, in the opinion of qualified authorities. Reasons given: 1) The inferior conditions under which Negroes have lived and still live, on the average; 2) discriminations against them, and less chance to get adequate legal help, which make them more likely than Whites to run afoul of laws, be arrested, convicted, sentenced; 3) various other environmental factors which work adversely against Negro family life, proper child rearing and individual adjustment. Wherever economic, educational and social conditions for Negroes improve, their crime rates drop.

▶ *Puerto Rican crime rate*. Currently there is concern in some American cities (New York and others) about the high crime and delinquency rates among recently arrived large groups of Puerto Ricans. Any thought that this is related to "natural" tendencies, or to anything other than their extremely underprivileged living conditions, is questionable. Few authorities doubt that, as with the Negroes, the crime rates among these new arrivals will drop as rapidly as their environments and opportunities improve.

SEX DIFFERENCES IN CRIME. Both heredity and environment are peculiarly interrelated in producing the vastly higher rate of crime among males than among females, and the differences in types of crime, as measured by arrests and convictions.

Figures for 1953 in the United States show eight times as many men as women arrested. For *murder,* the male rate was six times that of the female; for *burglary,* fifty times; *robbery,* twenty-two times; *forgery,* five times. Even then, this excess of male over female crime is much smaller than it was in former times, when women had less freedom to adopt men's bad habits and practices. But the question remains, whether training, moral codes and other conditioning factors can completely account for the sex differences in crime.

▶ *Natural physical factors.* The theory that men by nature are more inclined to commit crimes of violence than are women, everything else being equal, rests on these facts: 1) Among other animals—all mammals and most birds—males are inherently more aggressive, more given to violent behavior and harder to train or domesticate; 2) experiments with lower animals have shown a direct relationship between male hormones and aggressiveness: treating females (rats, hens, etc.) with male hormones makes them develop male aggressive and fighting qualities, while in males, subtracting male hormones through castration, or adding female hormones, tends to make them more passive and submissive; 3) in the youngest children one can note a greater tendency of boys to be aggressive, unruly and destructive; 4) superior strength and physical capacities of men lead them more into occupations inducing violence and familiarity with weapons; 5) differences in sexual functioning, in their natural parental roles and in the consequences of loose conduct, tend to make women more restrained than males in their behavior, and further differentiate their activities, opportunities and inclinations with respect to crime.

▶ *Temperamental factors.* The foregoing points, as noted, apply mainly to crimes involving physical acts. There is no evidence that nature or heredity have made women any more moral or "angelic" than men. The crimes of women almost always have tended to be more subtle, veiled and personal, and more likely to evade the meshes of the law, than those of men. But as their opportunities for open wrongdoing have increased, women's crime rates have shot upward. Thus, the introduction of firearms, eliminating the strength disadvantages, has caused a marked rise in murders by women; and occupational changes have greatly increased the convictions of women for theft, fraud, forgery, embezzlement, etc.

▶ *Sex crimes.* Differences in the sex organs and sex functioning of males and females lead naturally to differences in the types of sex crimes each might commit (mainly, *rape* by males and *prostitution* by females). Otherwise, however, there is little relationship between heredity and sex offenses. Nor, as a rule, are sex offenses linked with other types of crime, except insofar as criminal conduct or a criminal environment may also lead to looseness or viciousness in sexual conduct. This is especially true of prostitution. In countries where prostitutes are not regarded as criminal (or in some places not even looked down on), there may be nothing in the way of abnormal tendencies to turn them toward this profession. But wherever prostitution is condemned by law and society, and where it is conducted in a criminal atmosphere, women who go into it, and stay in it, do tend to have abnormal or criminal tendencies. However, prostitution by itself, and other sex offenses (including *homosexuality*) might be more properly considered as types of sexual behavior. (See next chapter.)

ALCOHOLISM. Most authorities now regard this not as a crime or any ordinary form of wrongdoing, but as a disease or personality disorder. At the same time, new theories have increased the possibility that heredity may be involved in *some* cases of alcoholism. That the condition is largely environmental is clearly shown by the enormous differences in the rate of alcoholism in various countries, nationalities, regions and social groups, as governed by their habits, attitudes and religious precepts; and by the great increase in alcoholism among women and young people since social codes became looser. However, to explain why in any group only *certain* individuals become alcoholics under the same conditions which leave others unaffected, recent studies indicate these possibilities: 1) That the chemical makeup of some individuals is such as to either induce an unusual craving for alcohol, perhaps because of certain dietary and vitamin deficiencies, or to cause them to react abnormally to its effects; and/or 2) that easily unbalanced mental and emotional states in some individuals predispose them to become alcoholics under little more than ordinary stresses. In either of these situations there could be hereditary factors producing or increasing the tendencies. For the present this is only theory. Until proved otherwise, one may assume that wherever alcoholism runs in a family (grandfather, father, son, mother, daughter, etc.), it is most likely that the members have *acquired* the habit from one another.

WAR. Most of the facts with respect to crime in individuals can be applied to refuting the theory that in mankind as a whole there are "mass criminal" or "murder" instincts, which must burst out periodically into war; and that these "instincts" for war or aggression are very strong in some nations, whereas peoples of other nations are by nature peaceful. This theory finds no support either in scientific studies or recent history. A first error is to assume that war is a "return to the animal state." Actually, while among lower animals *individuals* may fight, there is never any bloody mass conflict between two groups of the same species, as there is among human beings. Again, if in lower animals, those of different species or breeds are most antagonistic, so among humans one would expect any "war instinct" to show itself most between those of different races. Yet we know that many of the bloodiest wars in history have been between groups of the same race, and often also of the same stocks and nationalities (as in the civil wars in the United States and most recently, in Korea, Indo-China and China). Finally, the presumed "warlike" or "peaceful" nature of any people has often changed abruptly. Many primitive tribes (including American Indians) once considered "bloodthirsty savages" are now among the most peaceful of peoples. So, too, are the once-warlike Scandinavians. The Chinese, for centuries peaceful, are now highly war-minded. The Jews, warriors in biblical times, were long thereafter thought of as "non-fighters," but back in Israel have again become warriors. And so on. All of this has led the scientists who study human makeup to be among those most convinced that warfare lies not in our genes but in our thinking, and that if there is any "mass" instinct among human groups, it is for getting along with rather than killing one another.

This might even be applied to crimes by individuals: The strongest desire in everyone is to get along with others—to be loved and respected, to be given a chance to be useful, to "belong" and to join both in producing and receiving whatever the community can provide for happiness. It is only when individuals are in some way frustrated in achieving this end that they turn to crime.

24

Sex and
Sexual Behavior

THE SEX DIFFERENCES. The most important of all influences on behavior is a person's sex. Just as among lower animals the male and female of each species differ in their behavior in many ways, so do they also among human beings. These human behavior differences may be classed under two headings: 1) *Sex* behavior, referring to distinguishing traits of males as compared with females in actions, mannerisms, speech, movements, attitudes, etc.; 2) *Sexual* behavior, directly involving the sexual impulses, feelings and acts, as they reveal themselves in love-making, intercourse and other sexual outlets. Both types of behavior are the extremely complex results of an interplay between inborn tendencies and environmental influences. Our purpose in this chapter will be mainly to look for possible hereditary factors.

The Two Roads. At the moment of conception, as reported in Chapter 4, the "XY" sex chromosome combination of males, and the "XX" combination of females, start them off immediately on different developmental roads. Further, as reported in other chapters, with succeeding stages of development the sexes show marked differences in their growth rates, body form and functioning, onset of puberty, physical capacities, sexual organs, reproductive and parental roles, susceptibility to diseases and defects, aging effects and other biological manifestations. Not the least of these are the processes peculiar to women: menstruation, childbearing, child-nursing and the menopause. Even if every effort were made to equalize the external environments for both sexes, each of the factors mentioned would tend to produce some differences in the behavior of females generally as compared with males. However, we must not ignore the fact that environment may continually work to intensify and some-

196

times distort these differences through training, moral and religious codes, courtship patterns, marriage roles, jobs, styles, etc.

▶ *Hormonal factors.* Among the biological factors most directly affecting male and female behavior are the differences in the sex hormones—not in type, but in quantity. Males produce much more of the so-called "male" hormone—*androgen;* females produce much more of the so-called "female" hormone—*estrogen.* (Some of the other hormones—pituitary, adrenal, thyroid—also may be produced by the two sexes in different proportions.) In lower animals the sex-hormone effects on behavior are striking. In poultry, when young female chicks are dosed with male hormones, they begin to act like little roosters, showing sudden aggressiveness and trying to crow; grown hens, if deprived of female hormones, also take on rooster characteristics; and very young roosters, if castrated and deprived of male hormones, lose their "cockiness" and become feminized. In dogs, young female puppies if dosed with male hormones assume the male position in urinating (one hind leg raised, where female dogs otherwise squat). Also, in rats and guinea pigs, as well as poultry, individual animals who are aggressive and dominant over others can be made submissive by decreasing their male hormones and increasing their female hormones; or by the reverse process, submissive animals can be made aggressive and dominant.

▶ *Sex-hormone changes in humans.* Experiments such as those just mentioned have not, of course, been performed on human beings. However, certain diseases or defects which disturb and greatly change the balance of the sex hormones in either boys or girls can swerve their behavior patterns from what is usual for their sex. Most pronounced are the feminizing effects of castration on boys *before puberty.* Castration in maturity, when the masculine physical and behavior traits already have been set, produces only limited and gradual effects on behavior. Nevertheless, it will also be noted that as men age, and their output of male hormones decreases, they become progressively less "masculine" in behavior, and very old men may behave not too differently from old women. As for females, what corresponds to castration—removal of the ovaries—before puberty, may produce only slight behavior changes; and the changes may be even slighter, and only very gradual, if the operation is performed in maturity.

▶ *The menopause.* This also is called the "change of life" because it marks the natural end of the woman's reproductive, or possible further childbearing phase, although she may still be otherwise vigorous and healthy, and often quite young—sometimes well under forty. While behavior changes often accompany the menopause, and may result from the biological changes and transitions, the effects may be considerably intensified by the psychological state of the woman. As a rule, women who have previously been well balanced emotionally show little behavior change during and after the menopause.

▶ *Male "change of life."* There is little to show that men have anything equivalent to the female menopause. There is no abrupt stoppage in men of reproductive capacity, but rather a gradual diminution which is part of the general aging process. Any marked behavior changes which might also occur in a man during his late forties or in his fifties are quite likely to be almost entirely psychological, the results of his feeling that he is "losing his grip."

▶ *Abnormal sex development.* Many of the biological sex abnormalities discussed in Chapter 13, such as defects or peculiarities of the sex organs, retarded sex development, premature sex development, etc., obviously affect behavior. While heredity may play a part in some of these conditions, as explained, the effects on behavior result largely from the way the individual, and the family or outsiders, regard the biological abnormalities.

SEX AND PSYCHOLOGICAL TRAITS: Childhood. How far the many significant psychological, social and behavior differences observable between little boys and girls are due to inborn factors, or to the way they are trained, cannot be easily determined. As parents have observed, little boys as a rule tend to be more restless, active, aggressive, destructive and somewhat harder to manage. Little girls are usually more restrained, more self-sufficient and quieter in play, preferring dolls to mechanical toys; and after the age of two or three, they tend to be more aware of people, shyer, and perhaps more nervous (with more nail-biting and thumb-sucking) than boys. Also, as noted in Chapter 19, little girls show greater hand dexterity and independence in dressing themselves. At least some of these differences appearing in the first few years have been regarded as influenced by natural tendencies, because even among lower animals young males and females act differently in various ways. But undoubtedly, as childhood progresses, the ways in which boys and girls are reared would heavily accentuate and more strongly differentiate any of their inborn behavior differences.

"Masculinity" and "femininity" tests. Almost everywhere in the world the traits linked with males and most admired in them are strength, virility, bravery, aggressiveness, dominance, enterprise, adventurousness, interest in outdoor activity and ability to *do* things (particularly of a mechanical nature). Linked with and most admired in females are interest and proficiency in domestic activities (cooking, sewing, homemaking, child-rearing), tenderness, affection, sentimentality, sensitivity, etc. These trait distinctions provide the basis of the "M-F" tests devised by Professor Lewis M. Terman and others for measuring the relative degrees of "masculinity" and "femininity" shown by given individuals. But as indicated previously, there is much question as to the relationship between these test scores and the biological sex traits. One could argue that greater strength, aggressiveness, dominance and bravery in a physical sense could be more naturally characteristic of men, as they are of males among other species (bulls, roosters, stags, etc.). And again, traits such as tenderness and domesticity might also develop more naturally among women through their childbearing and child-rearing functions. Yet in a psychological sense there is no evidence at all that women cannot be and are not as brave, aggressive, enterprising and venturesome as men. If they reveal these qualities less it could be much more because of social influences than of their gene workings.

SEXUAL BEHAVIOR. As explained at the beginning of this chapter, *sexual* behavior refers specifically to the impulses, feelings and acts in any way connected with the sex organs and sexual outlets. This is an enormous subject. We must limit ourselves here to the possible hereditary aspects as they relate to individual differences in sexual behavior, and to those types of behavior which are markedly unusual and non-average, or "abnormal."

▶ *Socio-sexual development.* This refers to a human being's sexual behavior as it develops in relationship to other persons. In average individuals such sexual development proceeds through quite definite stages, as listed below; and it is when these stages are not properly experienced or completed that cause for concern, or suspicion of "abnormality," may arise.

1. Infancy and babyhood: Interest only in one's own sex organs and feelings. Individuals stopping at this stage are the *"narcissists"* who cannot show sexual feeling for anyone but themselves, and derive satisfaction only from their own bodies. Causes are probably psychological.

2. Early childhood: Play with members of the opposite sex, but without conscious sex interest. Those who do not outgrow this stage remain undeveloped in their sexual feelings and responses, and very low in sex-drive. While again the causes may be psychological, sometimes they are traceable to deficiencies or defects in the sex glands and organs, which may or may not have an hereditary basis. (See Chap. 13, "Sex Abnormalities.")

3. Ages six to ten (approximately): Interest only in those of one's own sex, and disinterest in or aversion to the opposite sex. Those remaining at this stage after puberty and into maturity may be in danger of developing into *homosexuals.* (See later discussion.)

4. Adolescence: Marked interest in the opposite sex, and an urge for sexual relationships, but with little discrimination and no desire for permanency. Those who do not pass beyond this stage may include, among males, the "Don Juans" and among females, the "nymphomaniacs"—persons constantly seeking new and frequent sexual partners because they lack mature sex feeling and never can obtain full satisfaction with anyone. Psychoanalysts also regard many Don Juans as suffering from partial impotency, or fear of impotency, and many of the nymphomaniacs as being *frigid* women. Inherent factors, such as glandular deficiencies or nerve defects, may be involved in certain of the

cases, but in most others the causes are chiefly or entirely psychological.

5. Maturity: Selection (where there is opportunity to do so) of one individual of the opposite sex as a permanent mate, not only for sexual union, but for marriage and establishing a home, family and social life. This is considered as the final—and socially approved—stage of sexual development in most civilizations. Whether it is also the "natural" final stage, dictated by inherited impulses, would be difficult to prove. At any rate, achievement of this stage is the standard by which "normal" adult sexual behavior is judged in the United States and many other countries.

THE KINSEY STUDIES. The voluminous and widely publicized reports on human sexual behavior by Professor Alfred C. Kinsey and his associates in recent years present detailed facts on the sex lives of more than fifteen thousand males and females. However, since the Kinsey studies have so far been concerned mainly with what human sexual behavior *is,* rather than what *causes* it, there is very little evidence in the reports that bears directly on hereditary aspects of human sexual behavior, and where such evidence is offered, there is question as to whether it can yet be accepted as scientific proof. Of chief interest here are the following Kinsey observations and conclusions, briefly summarized:

——The most important biologic factors affecting human sexual behavior are the hereditary forces which account for the differences between male and female. Within either sex, heredity must also account for some of the variation in sensory structures and mechanisms which affect sexual responses and performance.

——Males begin their active sexual lives much earlier than females, and reach their peak of sexual potency and expression at about age seventeen, whereas with females the sexual peak does not come until almost age thirty.

——The total lifetime sexual performance of an average male is vastly greater than that of the female, but some females are capable of enormously more sexual performance than males.

——Males by nature are much more stimulated sexually

through psychological influences than are females, are much more inclined to promiscuity, and require far more sexual expression.

——Many cases of *frigidity* in women may be due to the fact that they were "never equipped to respond erotically"; and among males, some cases of impotency or low sex-drive may also be the result of inherent factors.

——No type of sexual behavior in human beings can be considered "abnormal" or "unnatural," and if it were not for training to the contrary, almost every person would indulge in almost every type of sexual behavior.

Note: With respect to all of the foregoing statements, it must again be stressed that they cannot be accepted as established facts, for, although considered valid by some authorities, they have been challenged by others. Moreover, Dr. Kinsey himself has presented many of his findings as "tentative," pending further research.

HOMOSEXUALITY: Male. This condition has many puzzling and debatable aspects, particularly as related to the *overt* homosexuals—those who consistently and preferably turn for their sexual relationships to their own sex and who have many distinctive and easily recognizable mannerisms, "feminine" or otherwise. (Some overt homosexuals, however, are outwardly extremely masculine in appearance and actions.) The incidence of homosexuality is uncertain. In the sample of males who volunteered for the Kinsey interviews, 13 per cent were classed as "predominantly homosexual," and 4 per cent as exclusively so; but there is strong suspicion that the "Kinsey" males included disproportionate numbers of the non-average. Various other studies indicate that the true incidence of the more overt male homosexuals in the United States and elsewhere may approach 3 per cent.

▶ *Causes of homosexuality.* It is quite likely that different types and degrees of homosexuality may arise through different factors, psychological, social and biological. While most authorities stress the psychological influences, there is also some possibility of inborn quirks in homosexuality of the more overt types. As reasons: 1) Overt homosexuals have appeared among human beings throughout history and in the most diverse environments. 2) Many homosexuals everywhere, whether in the most primitive or the most civilized societies, show remarkable similarities in movements, mannerisms, vocal inflections and various other behavior traits. 3) They often seem to arise spontaneously, with tendencies shown in childhood, and with no conditioning factors that can explain them. 4) Studies of *twins*, by Dr. Franz J. Kallmann and others, show that in the great majority of cases where one of a pair of identical twins was homosexual, so was the other, but that this was not true of fraternal twins; and that 35 per cent of the twin homosexuals came from families where the trait had appeared in other members.

▶ *The "intersex" theory.* A few scientists have maintained that homosexuals of the extreme "invert" type (with "feminine" physical traits) may represent an in-between sex. In certain lower species one does find individuals in whom the sex chromosomes are out of balance, so that they are neither completely male nor completely female. But there is no proof that this happens in human beings, or if it does, that it would change the direction of a person's sex interests from the opposite sex toward his or her own sex. Another theory is that overt male homosexuals tend to be deficient in "male" sex hormones. But tests have not proved this to be so as a rule, nor have hormonal treatments been found to change homosexual impulses.

▶ *Conditioning factors.* Whether or not inborn tendencies or susceptibilities are involved in homosexuality, there is considerable evidence that specific environmental factors can do much to turn a person toward this behavior. Most often held responsible for male homosexuality are neurotic, sexually frustrated, dominant or clinging mothers, who seek to raise their boys as girls, and implant in them fear or distaste of opposite-sex relationships. However, there are many cases where such influences are lacking, and where it would be highly unfair to blame the parent. In any case, if the homosexually inclined individual is still young, or in an indecisive stage, there is a good chance of conditioning him toward normalcy. But in an adult, once the homosexual pattern has been strongly set, there is at present little evidence that it can be changed either by medical or psychological treatment.

Female homosexuality. The problem of female homosexuality is not as serious as that of male homosexuality because the incidence is much lower (probably under one per cent), it is much less on the surface, and its social effects are not as harmful. For one thing, the greater need and desire of women to marry and have children acts to suppress any homosexual tendencies in them more than in males. Otherwise most of the basic facts given for male homosexuality apply to the corresponding behavior in the female. Thus, while some female homosexuals are "masculine" in outward appearance and behavior, many others are completely feminine in all respects save their sexual inclinations (although they may have relationships with males as well as females). Again, some female homosexuals appear to be products solely of warped emotional or psychological conditioning, but others seem to have started with strong inner tendencies toward abnormal sexual behavior, which may or may not have had a biological basis. Finally, as with males, the chance for conditioning a homosexually inclined female toward normalcy depends largely on whether she is in the young and/or indecisive stage, or is adult and has already been strongly set in the homosexual pattern.

Prostitution and Sex Crimes. See Chap. 23.

25

Human Evolution

EVOLUTION. To understand how human beings originated on this earth, one must have some idea of how life of any kind first began and how it led to the development of all the countless types and forms of other living things. The process by which scientists believe this was achieved is called "*evolution.*" When people use this term they are apt to think of Charles Darwin, for it was his theories of evolution, published in 1859, which revised all previous concepts. What caused the most controversy and opposition was Darwin's contention that the different creatures were not created suddenly, at the same time, and in their existing forms, but developed step by step, over very long periods, from other and simpler types; and, specifically, that *human beings* had also developed from lower forms of animals.

▶ *The Bible and Darwin.* To many persons, the Darwinian theories may have seemed a direct contradiction of the biblical account of Creation as having taken place in six "days," and of man in one "day." But others have realized that there actually need be no real conflict on this point if one interprets the biblical "days" of Creation as meaning *stages* of indefinite length. By this definition modern science holds very closely in most respects to the biblical concept of the successive stages of Creation: 1) The earth being "without form, and void," then being shaped into a mass covered by water, with "light"—the heat and energy from the sun—a first essential in all that was to take place; 2) land rising from beneath the waters, forming continents and islands surrounded by oceans; 3) the growth of vegetation; 4) changes in climate, environments and food conditions; 5) the creation and existence of the simplest creatures, gradually developing into fish, reptiles, fowl and mammals; 6) finally the evolution (or creation) of man. If scientists think of this as happening not in a "week," but in vast stretches of time—three billion years or more—and in endlessly remarkable ways, it can only add to the wonder of Creation.

THE FIRST LIFE-SPARK. In explaining evolution, scientists begin with the assumption that the first living thing was a single cell consisting of a *single gene* housed in a blob of the life-stuff, protoplasm. (This cell may have come from a simpler, virus-like cell, in between living and non-living.) Endowed with the property of life and reproduction, the first gene cell could multiply itself endlessly. Very soon, among the millions of separate offspring cells, *mutations*—changes in genes (as described in Chapter 3)—began to take place, making some different from the others. As mutations increased, different genes began hooking up into chains to form chromosomes. And with each change in the types, numbers and varieties of genes and chromosomes, there also were changes in the types and complexities of the cell formations, and of the creatures they produced. Not least important was the creation of *two sexes*. At the beginning creatures reproduced by dividing themselves, so hereditary changes from one generation to another were limited. But when mutations produced "sex" genes, then sex chromosomes, and thus individuals of two sexes, this greatly extended the possibility of making new combinations of genes with each mating, and speeding up evolutionary changes.

▶ *"Inventive" mutations.* Altogether, in a rough way the process of evolution in living things was not too unlike that which came later in the evolution of man-made machines. From the first crude tools fashioned by man—chipped rocks—there evolved hand axes, spears, arrows, knives, needles and tools and devices of innumerable kinds. From the first simple wheel there evolved vehicles and machinery growing ever more complex, until, with the discovery of engines, there came automobiles and huge airplanes. Tree-trunk canoes to battleships, windmills to giant power plants, bullets to atomic bombs—all of these were the results of countless successive inventive mutations. So, too, all the varieties of living and growing things in our world today are the products of vastly more numerous and complex *genetic* mutations. Just to produce the human eye alone, for instance, must have required thousands of mutations over millions of years.

STEPS IN EVOLUTION. Aiding continuously in the processes of evolution has been the fact that as different mutations popped up, if they served some useful purpose or offered an advantage to a creature at a given time they survived. But where mutations produced a defect or disadvantage (true in the great majority of cases) the creatures died off. In this process of "selecting out" the good mutations and weeding out the bad ones, *environment* was always a factor. Each type or change of climate, food supply, natural hazard, enemy, disease, or other condition demanded something special in an animal for survival and development. Different mutations answered these needs, in the forms of particular kinds of bodies, feathers, furs, skins, claws, teeth, coloring, internal organs, breathing apparatus, sensory equipment (eyes, ears, sense of smell), and not least, *brains,* as well as many other details. But if the right mutations didn't come along, species of creatures could often also survive and thrive by *moving* to some new environments, or being moved there by the winds, water, earth upheavals or climatic changes. Either way, groups of creatures originally of similar types spread out and became *segregated* from one another. And again, over new long periods of time, in each group new mutations kept appearing, which, in their different environments, were selected out and adapted differently, making the isolated groups increasingly different from one another. These, plus other factors (including crossbreeding and various chance elements), can account for the innumerable kinds of birds, fishes, mammals and other animals, and the varieties of each species that are peculiar to given regions and localities the world over.

"Acquired Characteristics." The erroneous old theory that evolution proceeded because traits *acquired* by animals, through experiences and habits, were or could be inherited by their offspring, was briefly discussed in Chapter 2. Here are a few more points. The most questionable part of the theory is that what an animal needed or wanted—or no longer needed or wanted—could *cause* a particular mutation to take place. If giraffes had to keep stretching their necks to eat high up on trees, they would somehow cause their offspring to be born with longer and longer necks; or if animals stopped using some part of their body, their genes would stop providing it. But there is just no way of explaining *how* this could occur. If an animal kept stretching its neck, how could that shake up or change its "neck" genes so as to put more "stretch" in their workings? If a red bird was too easily spotted by enemies in green trees, how could that *make* its "color" genes begin to produce green feathers? Obviously this is impossible. The probable fact, as already indicated, is that in each species mutations of every conceivable kind kept coming along purely through chance (as they still do, which can be seen by observing flies, mice and other creatures in laboratories). With the desirable mutations being retained, the bad ones eliminated, for generation after generation, as one useful mutation was added to another, this could conceivably have produced in sufficient time any type of creature, or the particular inherited traits in all the creatures existing today.

▶ *Chicken or egg first?* The facts as science now gives them clearly answer that the *egg* came first. By the old "acquired-characteristic" theories it would have been the chicken: That is, one would start with a type of bird which, through gradual changes in habits and environments, presumably turned into a chicken, which *then* produced the characteristic chicken egg. But modern genetics holds that mutations kept producing different kinds of genes in eggs of a bird species, which in time caused these *eggs* to produce chickens. As applied to persons and eggs, for instance, a blue-eyed baby does not result because its parents were blue-eyed persons (often they are dark-eyed), but because the *egg* from which the baby came carried "blue-eye" genes. Originally it is possible that there were no human blue-eye genes and that one suddenly arose through mutation. Thus again it was not the blue-eyed person, but the "blue-eyed" *egg* which came first.

▶ *The Lysenko controversy.* This involves the revival of the "acquired-characteristic" theories by some Soviet plant breeders, led by Trofim Lysenko, and their attack on various principles of modern genetics. The attack, starting in the 1930s, led to the exiling of Russia's top geneticist, Vavilov, to Siberia (where he died in 1942), and the forced recantation of their scientific beliefs by many other Russian geneticists after the Societ Central Committee, in 1948, proclaimed the Lysenko theories as the only "correct and acceptable" ones. Lysenko's claims went farthest when he reported in 1949 that he had succeeded in *turning wheat into rye* by environmental changes—which, to geneticists, would seem as likely as causing cats to give birth to puppies by changing their diet and living conditions. However, by 1954 Soviet scientists were beginning to challenge Lysenko on his theories, although he was apparently still strong in his official position. Many believe his rise to power with Soviet political leaders came in part because of his success as a practical plant breeder, and in part because his claims offered support to the Marxist theories of the all-importance of environment. What seemed to have been overlooked was that if good environment could cause an improvement in the *heredity* of plants (or human beings), *bad environment* could cause a deterioration in heredity. And on that basis, the Russian people, long exposed to very bad environments, would have developed inferior hereditary traits—which, of course, is completely contrary to what modern genetics has established.

EVOLUTION OF "PRIMATES." The scientific story of human evolution begins perhaps 50,000,000 years ago. By that time the earth was teeming with creatures of every kind. Among them were some now called "primates," who were smarter and nimbler than other animals. In succeeding millions of years innumerable mutations produced different types and branches of the primate family. Some were the monkeys—lemurs, spider monkeys, macaques, baboons. From the more "intelligent" branches came the great apes—the gibbon, orangutan, chimpanzee and gorilla. And finally, from another *separate* branch, and "twigs" of this branch, there began to develop species of the brainiest of all creatures—*Man*. In other words, *human beings did not descend from apes,* but both apes and men came from the same "primate tree." So while we and the apes of today have common ancestors, our relationship is millions of years apart, and the best any ape can claim is that he and we are very, very distant "cousins."

▶ *Apes and humans.* With all the manifold differences, we nevertheless recognize that monkeys and apes are far more like us than are any other animals. That is why we are so fascinated watching them in zoos or on television, and why we call people we like "little monkeys," and those we don't, "apes," or "gorillas." From the scientific standpoint, the fact that human beings belong to the same primate family as do monkeys and apes is proved in a great many ways: By unique similarities in their skulls, bones, teeth, eyes, hands and feet, and internal organs; by menstruation in their females (the only lower animals among whom this occurs); by closely similar periods of gestation (eight months for apes); by late onset of puberty (age nine or ten for apes); and, most recently discovered and perhaps most important, by *blood types* (those in apes being almost exactly like the A, B, O, Rh and other blood groups in humans). The one tremendous difference, though, is in *brains.* Mainly it was the series of additional "brain" mutations on the human branch of the primate tree (plus improvements in the hands and skeletal framework) that carried men so far beyond all other creatures, and left the apes and monkeys almost back where they were millions of years ago.

Earliest Man-Types. Between the time that the man family began to evolve, far in the dimmest past, and the point where anything like true human beings appeared, there were a great many "experimental models" of ape-men, part-men, half-men and near-men, who died out or were killed off as improved types of man came along. We know of those man-types, fairly late in the procession (a million years or so ago), only through a scant few of their skulls and bones which have been found. These earliest man-creatures have been named after the places where relics were dug up: The "South African Ape Man" (or "Man-Ape"), the "Java Man," the "Pekin Man," the "Heidelberg Man," the "Swanscombe Man," etc. (The "Piltdown Man," once classed among these ancients, was proved in 1953 to have been a hoax whose bones had been faked and planted in England.) All of these were still heavy-browed, half-brained, stooped and clumsy beings. But by a hundred thousand years ago a man almost like ourselves—the "Neanderthal Man"—had appeared and was living

The Evolution of Apes and Man
(ACCORDING TO CURRENT THEORIES)

FIRST PRIMATE

LEMUR

TARSIOID

NEW-WORLD MONKEYS

MACAQUE

BABOON

OLD-WORLD MONKEYS

FORERUNNER OF APES AND MAN

GIBBON

ORANG-UTAN

THE GREAT APES
(EVOLVING SEPARATELY)

CHIMPANZEE

GORILLA

S. AFRICAN MAN-APES

JAVA AND PEKIN MAN

NEANDERTHAL MAN

HOMO SAPIENS

CAUCASIANS   NEGROES   MONGOLIANS   A.S.
ALL EXISTING PEOPLES FROM
SAME ORIGINAL ANCESTOR ABOVE

(From *The New* YOU AND HEREDITY. Copyright, 1950, by Amram Scheinfeld.)

in various parts of Africa, Europe and Asia. He was about 5 feet 3 inches tall, had a big brow, a heavy jaw and big teeth, but a good brain and capable hands, which enabled him to make wooden spears and flint tools, and to use fire. He also respectfully laid out his dead, and must have shown other human traits.

"Homo Sapiens." By about 50,000 B.C. a New Man of our own present species, *Homo sapiens* ("wise man"), had evolved, possibly first in the region of Mesopotamia (which is where the Garden of Eden, Adam's birthplace, is supposed to have been). He was so superior to other types of men in brain power and skill that in time he alone survived. He may have killed off the cruder existing types of men (such as the Neanderthalers), or absorbed them by breeding; or they may have died off because of new diseases or conditions. About that we can only guess. But what we do know, from many scientific studies, tests and observations is this: All the human beings in the world today, of all races and in all places, are biologically and genetically so much alike that they must be descendants of the same original stock of *Homo sapiens*. No matter how different they may seem to be (for example, tall blond Nordics and African Pygmies), they all carry similar twenty-four pairs of human chromosomes with matching genes, and can mate and be fertile with one another (which would be impossible were they of different species). Thus, science now corroborates what most great religions have long been preaching: *Human beings of all races are equal "Children of God," descended from the same First Man.*

26
The Human Races,
I: Physical Differences

THE ORIGIN OF RACES. Knowing that all human beings are of exactly the same species, descended from the same original Man, how explain the many differences among them in features, coloring and other physical traits, as well as in behavior, culture and achievement? For the answer we return to the very beginnings of our species—*Homo sapiens,* about fifty thousand years ago, and trace the story of racial differentiation as science now sees it. Starting with a single fruitful couple (Adam and Eve, if you wish), favorable conditions could have resulted in close to a million descendants in less than a thousand years. But in those early periods, with no fixed habitats, large groups would not have held together. So, moving wherever climate and the search for food led them, bands of people would have drifted apart, losing contact with one another, and spreading eventually to all habitable places of the earth. In time, then, these isolated human groups, multiplying and becoming fixed in different environments for thousands of years, would have developed various special hereditary characteristics through the continuing processes of evolution. We noted in the last chapter how *selection* and *adaptation* of gene changes as they came along in different environments, plus chance factors, could produce many varieties of birds or other animals of each species. The same factors could just as easily produce the many physical differences among human racial groups. (Their cultural and behavior differences, however, must be explained in other ways, to be dealt with later.)

THE MAIN RACES. The word "race" can be applied only loosely to human beings, because there are no large human groups all of whose members are completely different in any one trait from all those of other racial groups. We can make racial distinctions only with respect to *average* differences in a given number of inherited traits, to the extent that they occur in markedly different proportions in different groups. On this basis most scientists classify all human beings into four primary, or main races (with the popular names given in parenthesis):

1. *Caucasoid* (or "White") race, developing and concentrated largely in Europe, Asia Minor, India and parts of North Africa. It is not known whether the White race was the first to develop; many authorities think the first members of *Homo sapiens* were dark, with Negroid features.

2. *Negroid* ("Black") race, developing and concentrated largely in Africa, later spreading to some adjoining regions and then also being carried to the Americas and the West Indies.

3. *Mongoloid* ("Yellow," or "Yellow-Brown") race, developing and concentrated mainly in Asia, and islands or regions adjoining it. Mongoloids are considered "younger" in evolutionary origin than either the Whites or the Negroes.

4. *Australoid* race, comprising primitive peoples in and around Australia, with origins not too certain, but believed to stem from a very early mixture of Negroid and Mongoloid, and also some Caucasoid stocks.

The classifications by skin color, it should be kept in mind, are very questionable. As was pointed out in Chapter 8, people of all races have the same skin pigments, though in different proportions. "Whites," for instance, are clearly not "white"-skinned. (They would look ghastly if they were.) What they themselves call their "flesh color," is actually pinkish-brown, as shown by the face powder or adhesive finger bandages they use. Further, many Whites, such as swarthy Latins and Arabs, are very dark, and some in India have skins much blacker than many Negroes. Nor is "Black" a correct term for many Negroid peoples who, without any mixture of White genes, have light-brown skins. So, too, the Mongoloids have a considerable range of skin colors, and while to some eyes their skins might seem to have a slight "yellowish" cast, this is only a variation of the basic human brown color.

▶ *"Ape-like" features.* An old, false theory is that people of some races can be proved to be "less human" than others because their features are more "ape-like." Although comparisons on this point have little meaning, it can easily be shown that persons of each race have some features which are farthest from the ape form, and some closest to it. For instance, the kinky hair of Negroes is less ape-like than the straight or wavy hair of Whites, and the sparse body hair of Negroes and Chinese is less ape-like than the hairiness of Whites. The full lips of Negroes put them farther away from the thin-lipped apes than are Whites. This no more proves that Whites are most "ape-like" than broad noses of Negroes prove Negroes are, or Eskimos' thin noses prove they're least so.

SUB-RACES. Each main race has (and had originally or developed in time) various sub-groups, some being offshoots from the main race, and others blends with other races. Some examples:

▶ *American Indians and Eskimos.* These are Mongoloid offshoots who, starting perhaps 25,000 years ago, began crossing over from Asia by way of a narrow strip of land then connecting Siberia with Alaska. The Mongols who formed or developed into the Eskimos and the various Indian tribes of North, Central and South America (including the Incas and Aztecs), did not come all at once, but separately, at long intervals, and where they show marked differences were probably already different Mongolian sub-groups when they started out from Asia.

▶ *The Negroes.* A common error is to think of Negroes in Africa (or in the United States) as all of one racial stock. Actually, they are of many racial sub-groups, with differences going back thousands of years and greater than are found among Whites. Some of the most striking differences are those between the tall, spindly, seven-foot Watusis of East Africa, and the stocky Pygmies of the Congo, while the Bushmen-Hottentots of South Africa are so different in many respects from other Negroids that some anthropologists believe they constitute a separate race. Other African Negroes, the Zulus (Bantus), Sudanese, etc., also have distinctive physical traits. Thus, since American Negroes, whose ancestors were taken from many parts of Africa, are mixtures of many Negroid strains, plus some amounts of Indian and

White genes, they might be considered in the mass as a new Negro sub-race, genetically different from all other Negro sub-races.

▶ *The Japanese*. While a sub-group of the Mongoloids, as are also the Chinese, the Japanese are distinct in various racial respects from other Mongols. One fact is their part-White ancestry through the Ainus, a short, hairy, Caucasoid people who may once have been quite prevalent from Russia to northern Asia, and primitive remnants of whom still live in northern Japanese islands. Also mixed in with the Japanese strain are genes from various Pacific islanders.

EUROPEAN "ETHNIC" GROUPS. When peoples are distinguished from one another less by inherited factors than by differences in culture, history and nationality, they are referred to as "ethnic" groups. "Ethnic" is often confused with "racial" (as are environmental traits with hereditary traits), especially as applied to European peoples. Thus, mistaken references often are made to the "Nordic," "Baltic," "Alpine," and "Mediterranean" "races," when they actually are ethnic groups with few clear-cut genetic differences among them. This is seen when we look into the origins of Europeans and find they are all highly mixed peoples, not at all "pure" Whites, but having both Mongoloid genes, brought in through early Hun and African invasions, and also some Negro genes brought in at various other times. Here are some of the mixtures that went into the principal European nationalities:

▶ *English:* Ancient Celts, Romans (and mixed Mediterraneans including North Africans), Anglo-Saxons, Danish Vikings, Normans, Germans.

▶ *Irish:* Ancient Picts, ancient peoples from France, Denmark, the Rhine (Celts) and Spain, Scandinavians, Normans, etc.

▶ *Germans:* Unknown primitive tribes, ancient Celts, Romans, Huns, Slavs, Franks and Saxons, Vikings, Huguenots.

▶ *Norwegians and Swedes:* Early Germanic tribes (through Denmark), Finns, Teutons, Lapps.

▶ *French:* North Africans, North Italians, Celts (Gauls), Romans, Germanic tribes, Huns, Norsemen, English.

▶ *Italians:* Ancient Sabines, Phoenicians, Etruscans, Greeks,

Gauls, Goths, Lombards, Normans, German-Swabians, French.

▶ *Spanish:* Iberians (from North Africa), Celts, Greeks, Carthaginians, Romans (Visigoths), Germanic peoples, Moors.

▶ *Russians:* Finns, early Germanic tribes, Huns, Slavs, Turk-Tartaric peoples, Tartars, Vikings, Germans.

▶ *Hungarians:* Celts, Romans, Vandals, Germanic Lombards and Goths, Huns and Avars, Slavs, Italians, French, Germans, Tartars, Turks.

"KITHS." Some anthropologists believe this term may be applied to certain large groups of humans who are a sort of cross between "ethnic" and "racial": that is, while originally of mixed stocks, they have held together for a long enough time, like large family groups, to develop various average hereditary similarities as well as common religious and cultural traits. Thus, the Jews, Irish, Scotch and Roumanians are considered examples of "kiths."

▶ *The Jews.* That the Jews definitely do not constitute a "racial" group, but can be described more as a "kith," is clearly shown by those collected in Israel today. The marked differences in physical appearance, features and coloring among the various groups—Yemenite, Moroccan, Polish, Russian, Roumanian, German, Spanish, Italian, Syrian, English and American Jews—not only reflect the different countries and environments from which they came, but also are proof that they are *genetically* different in various ways. Explaining this is the fact that continually through their wanderings they have absorbed genes of other peoples among whom they have lived (through converts to their religion, intermarriages, sometimes rape of their women, etc.). It is true that on the average some genetic characteristics are more common among Jews than non-Jews. But in any Jewish population a very large proportion of the individuals can in no sense be identified as "Jewish" by any physical traits, and this proportion is growing, especially in new generations of Jews in the United States and other countries, as their training and living conditions become like those of other groups. (Supposed distinguishing features of Americans of Irish, Scotch and other "kiths" are also becoming less and less marked in the newer generations.) Even in Israel visitors are struck by the fact that so many of the younger, native-born Jews ("Sabras"), reared and working in the Israeli farming communities, look so "non-Jewish" by former stereotyped ideas.

REASONS FOR RACE DIFFERENCES. As previously indicated, many of the main differences among races in coloring, features and even body types, may well have evolved because they served some useful purpose in their original environments. As with lower animals, in early human history it may have been a matter of life and death whether individuals and groups had this or that type of physical equipment to cope with existing conditions. (Even in the United States today many people move from North to South, or vice versa, or from some other region to another, because they "can't stand the climate" where they are.) Thus, it is not mere coincidence that the darkest-skinned, blackest-eyed peoples arose and were long concentrated in the hottest climates (and for the most part still live there), while the lightest-skinned and lightest-eyed peoples developed and live in the more temperate regions. Although great improvements in housing, heating, refrigeration, clothing and drugs, and in industrial devices, have reduced the early importance of inherited race differences in various environments, they still have their usefulness, or may prove to be more useful than we have believed. Here are some recent scientific findings on these points:

▶ *Coloring.* Negroes (and dark-skinned Whites, such as those in India, the Arab countries and North Africa) are best protected against the hot (ultraviolet) rays of the sun because of the heavier underlying deposit of melanin pigment particles in their skins. (Chap. 8.) Moreover, Negroes with the heaviest pigmentation have been found less likely than Whites to develop skin cancer in the tropics; also, because Negro skin has an extra outer protecting layer, it is more resistant to germs and infections in hot, damp tropical climates, and to scratches in the jungles. Whites, on the other hand, have an advantage in cooler climates because their more lightly pigmented skins permit a maximum of the beneficial vitamin D irradiation from the sun. (The in-between, yellow-brown skin of the Mongolians or bronzed skin of American Indians may also offer some advantages in their native environments, but this has not been established.) Again, the heavily pigmented Negro eyes, with added pigment inside the retina and in the eyelids, are better adapted than White eyes to the glaring tropics.

▶ *Structural details.* The broader nostrils of the Negroes may permit better breathing in hot, moist climates, whereas in cool regions the smaller, narrower White nostrils are better adapted to warming up cold air before it enters the lungs. The Eskimos, it may be noted, have among the narrowest of noses. But also, some authorities believe, Eskimos have been aided in adapting to arctic cold by their fatty eyelids and underlayers of other facial as well as body fat, and by their stocky figures and stubby limbs and hands which do not permit as much heat evaporation as do long, thin legs. Contrariwise, the spindly legs, long, thin hands and lanky figures of many Negroes are better adapted to heat evaporation in hot climates. In the matter of leg structure, some authorities believe that the particular formation and musculature of the legs of some strains of Negroes may be assets in running ability, and may partly explain the upsurge of Negro champions in track and racing events, once they have had the chance to train and compete. It is also possible that the tightly curled or kinky Negroid hair may permit better scalp ventilation in the tropics.

▶ *Uncertain factors.* In addition to the race differences mentioned there are others, some brought to light only recently (such as the blood types), whose usefulness or "adaptive" value remains uncertain or unknown. The Mongolian skin fold at the eye corner, some authorities believe, may help in protecting the eyes from the glare of the sun (or, with Eskimos, from ice and snow glare) by narrowing the slits through which the eyes are exposed. However, no good guesses have been made as to why Mongolians have such scant facial and body hair, or thick, black straight hair. Or why Negroes have thick lips. Or, among Whites, what practical advantage or disadvantage there may be in straight hair, or wavy or curly, or brown, red or blond hair. Or why women of some racial groups have much larger breasts, or different breast shapes, or more heavily padded buttocks, than others. Or why head shapes differ on the average among races. Many of these differences may be merely the results of Nature's decorative whims, unrelated to usefulness; or they may prove to have once had practical value, in given environments, or to be related to some internal chemical or functional traits which still have meaning.

BLOOD-TYPE DIFFERENCES. Just as individuals and families differ in their blood types (*A, B, O,* or the "Rh" groups, or "*M-N*" types, discussed in Chapter 15), there are blood-type differences—though only in *average* incidences—among racial and ethnic groups. These differences have nothing to do with blood "quality" or "strength," but are of interest to anthropologists because of the clues they offer in tracing the origins and relationships of racial and ethnic groups, and may also be useful legally in disputed paternity cases. The layman, however, can be only mildly interested in such facts as that the *O* blood type occurs in 46 per cent of the English, 50 per cent of the Spaniards, 29 per cent of the Japanese, 61 per cent of the Ethiopians and in almost 100 per cent of some pure American Indian tribes; that blood type *B* is most common among Asiatics and less frequent among Europeans; that blood type *A* ranges from up to 50 per cent among Europeans to 15 per cent among Filipinos; or that the "*M*" and "*N*" types have such and such racial incidences. With respect to Whites and Negroes, a new finding (1955) is that in addition to the much lower Rh-negative incidence among Negroes, a majority of them carry an Rh blood-group antigen called "*V,*" inherited as a dominant, whereas this is present in hardly 1 in 100 Whites.

DISEASE DIFFERENCES IN RACES. Because living conditions, diets, hygiene and other factors may vary greatly among racial and ethnic groups, it is often hard to tell whether or not heredity plays any important part in the different incidences of given diseases among them. We mentioned this with respect to Americans of different stocks (Chap. 18, "Race differences"). However, it was noted in the disease chapters that *Cooley's anemia* is largely confined to Mediterranean Whites, and *sicklemia* to Negroes (Chap. 15). Also, that *color blindness* is twice as common among Whites as among Negroes (Chap. 14). Certain very rare diseases and defects have been found confined largely to small groups within one race or another, which is not surprising if the conditions arose through unusual mutations in comparatively recent times. Again, it is possible that some racial groups, through evolutionary changes, have developed special resistance to certain infectious diseases peculiar to their original environments, and are more susceptible to diseases of other environments. But on the whole, virtually all types of inherited diseases and defects are found among all racial groups, and where conditions are approximately the same, the major diseases (cancer, heart afflictions, diabetes, etc.) appear in much the same proportions.

Miscellaneous race differences. *Tasting:* With respect to inherited differences in tasting the "PTC" chemical (Chap. 14), the incidence of "tasters" has been reported as 96 per cent among African Negroes, 94 per cent among Chinese, 70 per cent among American Whites and 63 per cent among Arabs. *Body chemistry:* Certain differences have been reported (1955) between Chinese and European Whites in normal excretions of amino acids (as shown through urinalyses), these differences being attributed not to diet but to inherited factors. *Fingerprints:* There are race differences in the relative incidences of whorls, loops and arch. Whorls, for instance, are found in 25 per cent of the English, 45 per cent of Japanese and 30 per cent of Jamaican Negroes.

27

The Human Races,
II: Qualities

RACIAL QUALITIES. Of all the facts dealt with in this book, what many persons may find hardest to accept is this: That no race, ethnic group or nationality (and specifically, their own) can be proved *better by heredity* in character or quality than any other. This statement strikes at deep-rooted conceits and prejudices that have caused countless bloody conflicts, that have brought death or suffering to untold millions of people, and that have been used to justify the enslavement or subjugation of some groups by other groups—not only in the past but in our own time, and at this moment. Fortunately, there is a growing realization that if mankind is to have a happier and more peaceful future, the peoples of the world must root out their old racial biases and adjust to the truths about themselves which science has been revealing. The most important of these truths we will try to present here.

Racial "Stereotypes." The term "stereotype" is applied to particular traits of temperament popularly associated with specific racial or ethnic groups: The English, "cool, reserved"; Germans, "militaristic," "systematic"; Latins, "excitable"; Irish, "pugnacious"; Swedes, "stolid"; Negroes, "childlike, uninhibited"; Chinese, "inscrutable"; Japanese, "sly"; etc. Whatever limited truth there may be in these "stereotypes" in any general sense, it is certain that they do not apply to a great many individuals of each racial group, and in all probability have no hereditary basis. On the contrary, there is every likelihood that these group traits are purely the products of environment, habits and training. This is clearly indicated in the United States by the fact that in a comparatively short time descendants of all races and nationalities have shed most of their supposed ancestral traits and taken on common characteristics of personality and temperament which peoples of other countries quickly identify as "American." (A significant story in reverse, of how an American who had been taken to China as a baby and reared there until age twenty, developed many characteristic "Chinese" traits, is told in the author's book, "*The New* You and Heredity," pp. 505-6.)

RACIAL CAPACITIES. The question of whether there are any racial differences in "minds," or in types or degrees of capacity for various tasks, cannot be answered precisely, first, because environments are and have been so different for people of different groups; and second (as noted in Chapter 19), there are as yet no scientific tests by which their relative *inherited* mental capacities can be accurately determined. Theoretically it is possible that certain types of "achievement" genes were at a given period, or may even now be, concentrated more heavily in one racial group than another. But the belief that any racial group is unique with respect to the genes for talent, skill or achievement as a whole is refuted by history, past and present.

▶ *Achievement differences.* During the thousands of years of man's cultural evolution, there has been virtually no racial group which at one time or another has not contributed greatly to progress in invention, industry, art, religion, science, social organization and other fields. Changing places at the head of the historical procession of conquerors and cultural leaders have been Semites, Mongols, Egyptians, Greeks, Romans, Turks, Moors and so on. And repeatedly, those out in front at one period fell behind later, and peoples who had long been backward or stagnant suddenly forged ahead of others. Even the so-called "primitives" in the heart of Africa had (as they still have) highly organized political and social systems, and had created intricate and beautiful works of art, far back at a time when many European peoples were much less advanced. Most recently we have seen the Japanese, Chinese, Hawaiians, Filipinos and many other groups in Asia, and also Africa, prove within a generation or two that they could brush aside supposed inborn shortcomings and master the most complex modern technical "know-how" in short order. Similarly, wherever training and opportunities of peoples of any kind have begun to be equalized, their achievements, too, have approached more and more the same levels. (*See also:* "Race Differences in Intelligence," Chap. 19; "Race Differences in Musicality," Chap. 20; "Racial and Ethnic Differences in Crime," Chap. 23.)

RACIAL "SUPERIORITY." The belief that one racial group is by *inheritance* "superior" in "blood" and character, and destined by nature to dominate "inferior" races, dates back actually no more than a century or two. Among ancient peoples there was no such race consciousness or prejudice. Kings would marry princesses of any other races, and Caesar hardly felt superior to Cleopatra, nor Solomon to the dark Queen of Sheba. Divisions among ancient peoples were tribal or political rather than racial. For instance, the biblical Hebrews thought of themselves as a "chosen people" mainly in the cultural and religious sense, and did not regard alien peoples as biologically inferior, nor ban intermarriage with those of other racial stocks who adopted their religion. Nor is there any evidence of any inborn or "instinctive" antagonism between racial groups. On the contrary, science has shown that people have to be *taught* to hate and look down on persons of other races, and that without this training White children, for instance, would no more shun Black or Yellow children than white birds, cats or dogs shun those of other colors. As it happens, racial antagonism in recent times has stemmed mainly from Whites. When African Negroes and American Indians first met Whites they were very friendly; even today, "race prejudices" refer chiefly to the attitudes of Whites towards those of other races. (*See also:* "War," Chap. 23.)

▶ *The Hitlerian hysteria.* An astounding and appalling fact is that at a time when myths about race had been exploded by modern science, racial fanaticism reached its most dreadful extreme in one of the presumably most advanced countries, Germany. Millions of people died, and millions more suffered horribly, before Hitler's reign of terror ended. That this was due purely to a "psychological sickness" in a warped environment is clear today, for there is no question that the German people are not *by heredity* any more cruel, militaristic or intolerant than others. (Chap. 23.) But unfortunately it is not all past history, because the poisons of racial prejudice engendered by the

Nazis have by no means been eradicated, and their false concepts continue to do harm.

▶ *Nazi racial theories.* We have already shown that the basic Nazi ideas—that the Germans constituted a "race" of "superior blood"—were scientifically preposterous, since the Germans were (to cite three of their own top anthropologists, Baur, Fischer and Lenz) no more than a "mish-mash" or compound of many racial strains. (Chap. 26.) But also, the terms "Aryan," used by the Nazis to describe their "race," and "non-Aryan," to describe Jews and others, actually had no racial meaning, having been coined by scientists for the classification of large groups of *languages.* Thus, "Aryan" takes in not only many European languages, but also the Vedda tongue spoken by Negroes in Ceylon. Likewise, "non-Aryan" refers to various other languages, including Arabic and Hebrew. But European Jews, who were the principal Nazi victims, were almost entirely *"Aryan"* in their language, since the overwhelming majority spoke not Hebrew but Yiddish—compounded of various European languages, mainly with an old German, and therefore *"Aryan"* base—as well as the language of the country in which they lived. The Nazi racial doctrine reached its silliest stage when Nazi scientists obligingly proclaimed their allies, the Japanese, as also "Aryans."

RACE MIXING. The strong feelings on this subject have been due to several beliefs. *One,* which we have just shown to be highly questionable, is that a given racial group is "superior" to another and will deteriorate if genes from an "inferior" racial group are mixed in with it. *Two,* that if races are kept "pure" they will each be more outstanding in particular ways (presumably as pure breeds of cattle, horses or dogs are each better for their particular purposes). But again, we have seen that no human racial groups are "pure," or ever have been or could be bred for "purity" the way domesticated animals have been. If at a given time any human group was or is "superior" in any respects, one could as easily ascribe this to their having been not pure but mixed, as in the case of Americans, one of the least racially "pure" and most genetically mixed nationalities the world has seen. *Three* is an old belief that crossbreeding between different human racial strains may result in misshapen offspring. But this also is contradicted by the many fine looking Mulattoes in the United States and South America (including some of the most beautiful actresses) and by handsome cross-breeds of many racial strains in Hawaii and elsewhere.

▶ *"Hybrid vigor."* Opposite to the anti-crossbreeding theories is the one that crossing different strains may produce hybrid off-spring with greater vigor and other advantages. Livestock and plant breeders have long employed this principle to advantage in combining desirable genes from two different stocks. In early human evolution the same principle might have been effective, but with respect to the present situation we can only make these deductions as to when and how crossing between genetically different groups might be beneficial: 1) If a highly desirable trait (better physique, more efficient internal organs, a special talent, etc.) could be produced by a combination of genes only some of which were carried by one racial group and the rest by another, so that crossbreeding could bring the needed genes to-gether; or, 2) if one group had some hereditary weaknesses and the other group carried "gene antidotes" for it. However, in the matter of race-crossing (or intermarriage) we are confining ourselves here only to the genetic aspects. The question of whether these matings are socially desirable, when they might lead to family and group conflicts, or personal maladjustment, is outside the field of this book.

▶ *Negro-White mixing.* Although many assume that Negro-White mixing has been highest in recent generations, the most race mixing actually took place in the Colonial days and up to the end of the Civil War. Moreover, where the earlier flow was of White genes into the Negro population, there has since been a considerable backflow of these White genes, plus some Negro genes, into the White population, by way of persons of mixed ancestry who could "pass." No accurate figures are available, but estimates (highly uncertain) are that perhaps two million persons of part-Negro descent are now in our White popula-tion, and that fifteen thousand or more go over to the White side each year. Since the genes for lighter skin and the less Negroid features are the ones being carried out of the Negro population, this should act to make American Negroes as a group darker and more Negroid, instead of less so, and to keep them racially distinct from the Whites for a long time to come. At present it is estimated that the American Negro population has from 20 to 25 per cent White genes. In addition, it may carry a small percentage of American Indian genes—probably much less than 1 per cent.

IS HUMAN EVOLUTION CONTINUING? Yes, but not necessarily at the rate it once did, nor in the same way, for a number of reasons: 1) In the earlier stages of man's evolution, more unsettled climatic conditions, higher temperatures and more intense radiation may have induced more frequent gene changes; 2) human groups have ceased being isolated as they once were for very long periods, which gave greater chance for new hereditary traits to become adapted and fixed in given environments; 3) the process of selecting out for survival the "fittest" persons, or those with special hereditary traits, has been greatly held down by social changes which permit individuals of all types and kinds (including genetic defectives) to survive and reproduce themselves. (See also Chap. 30—"Eugenics.") However, new mutations have been constantly occurring in humans (Chap. 3), perhaps at the rate of one changed gene in at least every tenth egg or sperm; or, taking sperms and eggs together, at least one in every five fertilized eggs (or children) would be carrying some newly mutated gene. The great majority of these gene changes are very slight, and most are harmful—some extremely so, being newly produced genes for many of the serious hereditary diseases and defects we discussed in earlier chapters. Only here and there do *desirable* mutations occur, which, if the changed genes are passed on and multiply, might lead to hereditary improvements in people. But whatever new human evolutionary changes might have taken place in recent generations, they could hardly have been very great or easy to detect, considering that a century is the merest tick of time in the vast stretches of man's evolutionary history.

▶ *Continuing animal evolution.* In lower animals it has been much easier than in humans to see continuing evolution at work, because they have many more generations in a given period and are less flexible in their capacities to adjust to changed con-

ditions—especially those which are man-made. Thus, within our
own time, scores of bird and animal species or types have become extinct or nearly so: including in America alone the pas-
senger pigeon, great auk, heath hen, Louisiana whooping crane,
Maine mink, Eastern puma, and various types of bears, elks and
wolves. On the other hand, many *useful* new mutations in various animals have been taken advantage of by breeders, resulting
in new types of fox and mink furs, improved types of fowl and
cattle, and many new strains of laboratory animals (flies, mice,
guinea pigs, etc.). In plants, fruits, flowers and vegetables, innumerable new mutations in recent decades have also led to the
evolution of many important new varieties.

THE ATOMIC AND HYDROGEN BOMBS. The great fear
of scientists today is that human evolution may indeed be
speeded up—but in a horrible, reverse way—by the enormous
numbers of *harmful* new mutations which almost certainly would
be produced if hydrogen or atomic bombs were exploded in any
large numbers in a future all-out war. As far back as 1927, before atomic bombs were dreamed of, Professor Hermann J.
Muller proved that radiation with ordinary X-rays could increase
the natural mutation rate in fruit flies by *150 times*. Later experiments showed that radiation of mice and other mammals—
including man—would not only cause gene changes, but would
do so to a greater extent (perhaps ten times as much) as in flies.
All this has awesome significance with respect to the hydrogen
and atomic bombs (and worse still, the possible "cobalt" bomb),
for their powers to produce mutations are infinitely greater than
that of ordinary X-ray devices. Not only is it positive that many
persons immediately exposed to such bomb blasts would (if they
survived) suffer changes in their genes, but the "fallout"—the
"rain" of radiated particles set loose by the bomb blasts—could
spread afar through winds and waters, contaminating plants,
fish and food animals, and causing mutations among people over
vast areas. Another danger, even in peacetime, may come from
atomic-energy plants. Any careless exposure of personnel to
radiation, or careless disposal of irradiated waste products, might
easily increase the mutation rate. (It should be kept in mind
that under normal conditions mutations are constantly occurring.

The threat in atomic radiation is that of adding greatly and dangerously to the mutation rate.)

▶ *How "atomic" mutations are caused.* Changes in genes can be caused by atomic radiation (or ordinary X-rays) in two ways: 1) The radiation can act instantly, through direct hits on some genes which cause an upset or rearrangement in the atoms composing them, so as to alter their workings. Or 2) radiation particles (alpha, gamma, beta, and neutrons) after entering persons' bodies, may find their way into the bone marrow, and from there keep up a slow bombardment of the germ cells to produce later mutations. If the absorbed atomic radiation particles are not by themselves menacing, they can become so when added to the radiation previously absorbed by a person through exposure to X-rays and to natural cosmic rays.

▶ *Radiation effects on future children.* These effects should be distinguished from the immediate effects on unborn babies carried by pregnant mothers exposed to atomic radiation. Studies at Nagasaki and Hiroshima, Japan, after the atomic bomb blasts of 1945, showed that many fetuses were killed or damaged by radiation effects, but not too many malformed babies resulted. However, the *genetic* effects—changes in genes—are not likely to become greatly apparent until several generations have passed. This is because most mutations are 1) slight; or 2) *recessive* (requiring the coincidence of two of the same genes coming together in a child); or 3) if producing serious dominant effects, are comparatively rare. Thus, among families of bomb survivors in Japan, reports so far show only slight increases over the average incidence of inherited abnormalities and defects. But geneticists are quite sure that in later generations of these families, especially if persons with the same mutated genes marry, the genetic changes will be more evident. If any of the much more powerful new atomic and hydrogen bombs are dropped anywhere, the genetic effects should become alarmingly obvious.

▶ *Will there be "atomic freaks"?* The popular fears in this direction go beyond the probabilities. Actually, any mutations in human genes produced by atomic bombs would hardly be different from those produced under natural conditions, which have led to the many inherited diseases and defects and abnormalities we now have. What large-scale atomic radiation would do, most certainly, would be to increase greatly the proportions of individuals with these conditions in the future.

▶ *Could not "superior" humans result?* It is not impossible that among the "atomic" mutations some might be desirable, leading to improvements in hereditary traits. But as stressed before, mutations are to an overwhelming extent of harmful or defective types—by a ratio of up to 100 to 1 as compared with neutral or desirable ones—and before the "superior" mutations could take hold they might very likely be engulfed by the "bad" ones.

▶ *Are there men on other planets?* The odds are heavily against this—at least, if we're thinking of men much like ourselves. Most of the planets of which we have knowledge lack the atmospheric or climatic conditions needed to sustain any type of life similar to that on earth. Some astronomers think that Venus and Mars, and some zones on Mercury, have an environment in which animals might develop and thrive. But whether advanced types of living things could be sustained is a question. Apart from this, it would seem almost impossible that the very same special evolutionary processes and environmental conditions which produced human beings on this earth could have been duplicated on any other planet, so as to produce similar beings. Even on this earth, should a radical change in conditions wipe out human life (as it once did with dinosaurs), or should man exterminate himself by atomic warfare, scientists doubt greatly whether a species like *Homo sapiens* could again evolve through the chance processes of evolution. One thing seems certain: That mankind now holds its evolutionary future in its own hands. Whether it can turn from destroying its hereditary assets to improving them remains to be seen. (Further discussion under "Eugenics," in Chap. 30.)

28

Ancestors and
Relatives

"BLOOD" KINSHIP. The term "blood" is merely a symbol with respect to the relationship of one person to another, since blood itself carries no hereditary factors. No one *inherits* anyone else's blood. As noted in Chapter 2, not even the mother's blood passes on directly to the child she carries, her blood being broken down into its elements before reaching the fetus. From the beginning the developing baby manufactures his own blood, and often his blood may differ even in hereditary type (A, B, O, Rh, etc.) from that of the mother. (Chap. 15.) Thus, sayings such as "The child carries my blood," or "Noble blood flows in his veins," or "He has common blood," are without meaning so far as heredity goes. Equally wrong is the assumption that a person's blood carries any traits of character, as when one speaks of "impetuous blood," "tainted blood," "honest blood," etc. The process of heredity, it must always be kept in mind, is solely and entirely one of passing on and receiving chromosomes and their genes.

▶ *Ancestral relationships.* Everything any person can inherit from an ancestor must be in the chromosomes received from each parent. No trait of itself can "skip over" from an ancestor to a descendant. Only chromosomes can be passed along, and these may or may not be the ones carrying the genes which can reproduce the trait of some ancestor. How much of a person's heredity stems from any given ancestor depends entirely on how many of the genes of that ancestor he received at conception. The further back the ancestor, the fewer of his or her genes a person is likely to have received, to the point where one may have virtually no hereditary link with a remote ancestor, regardless of what the "family tree" might show.

Ancestry Theories: Old and New

"BLOOD" THEORY (wrong)	"JIG-SAW" THEORY (wrong)	"CHROMOSOME" THEORY (right)
"A person is a mixture of the blood of all of his ancestors. No matter how far back an ancestor, some of his blood flows in one's veins."	"A person's ancestry consists of so many parts of this or that: For example, one eighth Irish, one eighth Scotch, one sixteenth Italian."	"A person's ancestry consists solely of how many chromosomes of different ancestors he carries. If no chromosome came from an 'ancestor,' there is no hereditary link with him."

▶ *Estimating hereditary relationships.* The only thing about one's heredity of which one can be certain is that exactly half of one's chromosomes came from each parent—twenty-four from the father, and twenty-four from the mother. Tracing further back, the number of chromosomes from any given ancestor can only be guessed. For, as explained in Chapter 3, each set of twenty-four chromosomes contributed to a child by a parent may be any one of millions of different combinations of the chromosomes from that parent's parents. Theoretically the twenty-four chromosomes received from one's father should include twelve from his father (one's paternal grandfather) and twelve from his mother (one's paternal grandmother). But actually, any number over half or less than half might have come from either grandparent. For example, among the twenty-four chromosomes received from one's father there might be not twelve, but fifteen or sixteen of his father's, and only eight or nine of his mother's. Similarly, one might receive proportionately more chromosomes of one's maternal grandfather than of one's maternal grandmother, or vice versa. In extreme cases a person could conceivably have received not more than two or three of a given grandparent's chromosomes, which means that actual hereditary linkage with earlier ancestors on that side of the family might almost be broken off at that point. All we can go by, therefore, are these *average* possibilities of the number of chromosomes of each ancestor one may be carrying:

Grandparents:	Avg. of	¼, or 12 chromosomes from each	
Great-grandparents:	" "	⅛, or 6 " " "	
Grt.grt. " :	" "	⅟₁₆, or 3 " " "	
Grt.grt.grt. " :	" "	⅟₃₂—either 2 chromosomes, or only one from each.	

REMOTE ANCESTORS. Once one goes more than five generations back—beyond a great-great-great-grandparent—the chances become less and less of having a *full* chromosome of a given ancestor. Thus, in the case of a claimed ancestor six generations back (such as, for Americans today, a Revolutionary War hero) the odds would be eight to three against having received a full one of his chromosomes. For an ancestor of the early seventeenth century, such as a Pilgrim, the odds might be twenty to one, or even forty to one, against carrying a full one of his or her chromosomes. We speak of a "full" chromosome because *parts* of chromosomes might also be passed along. This involves a complex genetic process called *"chromosome crossover,"* whereby every so often when sperms or eggs are formed in parents, and two chromosomes of a pair twist around one another, matching sections may be exchanged, or "cross over," when the chromosomes break apart. Such exchanges of parts of chromosomes over generations increase the chance that a person will have received at least a few of the genes of a distant ancestor. (See also section following.)

The "Cross-Over" Process

How one can inherit part of a chromosome

During the egg-forming or sperm-forming process, the paired chromosomes from the two parents may twist around one another.

In breaking loose, matching sections of the two chromosomes may be exchanged, so the new chromosomes formed thereafter have parts from different ancestors.

▶ *Increased chances of descent.* When in any lineage there have been marriages between persons with the same ancestor, the chances of a descendant having received chromosomes of that ancestor are increased. For instance, if one's parents had an ancestor in common, this would double the chance of one's having received some of that ancestor's chromosomes. The more marriages between relatives there were along the lines of descent in a family, the more closely those coming later in the lineage would be linked to earlier ancestors. Thus, present-day members of the much-intermarried European royal families (such as children of Britain's Queen Elizabeth and her husband, Prince Philip, both descendants of Queen Victoria), have much closer ties to remote ancestors than have persons in general. This also applies, in a more limited degree, to descendants of any non-royal close-knit groups among which marriages between near relatives were formerly common. (Colonial Americans, and members of many small communities in Europe, were among these.) Going back far enough into any lineage, of course, there must have been many marriages between relatives, for otherwise the number of anyone's potential ancestors—doubling with each generation back—would eventually reach astronomical and impossible proportions. Thus, it is estimated that all persons of English descent are at least thirtieth cousins; that there is fully as close a relationship within most other European stocks; and that with some smaller groups, such as the Swiss, Swedes, Danes, Dutch, Scotch, Irish, German Jews, etc., the cousin-relationship for almost all may be no less than the twentieth degree.

"Distinguished" ancestry. People who boast of descent from some famous remote ancestor usually overlook a number of the points we have stressed: 1) They ignore almost all the many other unknown ancestors who lived at the same time as the famous one, and who contributed equally to their heritage; 2) they may have received not a single one of the noted "ancestor's" chromosomes (or only a small part of one), and thus have virtually no hereditary link with him; 3) if they did get some of the ancestor's genes, these may not at all have been those which helped produce his admirable qualities, but may as easily have been his worst ones; 4) traits such as high intelligence, courage, or unusual talent of any kind are so complex that it would be impossible for any combination of genes producing them to be passed along intact from a given ancestor—perhaps not even from a grandparent. The situation might be different for persons who have not one or two, but many distinguished and worthy ancestors, and in whose family line for successive generations up to the present, there were marriages between persons of unusual character and ability. In such cases the descendants might have well above average chances of carrying "superior" genes. (See Chap. 20.) But rarely do "superior" marriages or "superior" offspring continue for too long in any one family line. No human families ever have been or could be bred as were domestic animals—horses, dogs, cattle, poultry—with thoroughbred strains being produced by mating mothers to sons, fathers to daughters, or brothers to sisters, and selecting only those with the particular traits desired and discarding the rest. Because human beings have always mated any which way, there is no family that can consider itself as genetically anything but a "mongrel" mixture, with most of its genes unknown. In any individual case, human "superiority" or uniqueness rests not in one's claim to distinguished ancestry, but only in what one can prove himself to be in character and achievement.

"Inferior" ancestry: "Jukes" and "Kallikaks." The many past misconceptions about "superior" ancestry were accompanied by equal misconceptions about "inferior" ancestry. In most countries certain family groups were held up (or still are) as horrible examples of inferior heredity. Most often cited in the United States were the "Jukes," first brought to public attention in 1874, and the "Kallikaks," publicized in 1912. Both families were reported as abounding in mentally defective, insane, alcoholic, degenerate, criminal, immoral, shiftless and undesirable individuals of every kind—which was blamed almost entirely on their presumed "inferior" and "tainted" heredity, in turn attributed mainly to a few degenerate ancestors four or five generations back. Modern science sees the facts in a different light. What appears probable is that 1) the case histories of these families were considerably exaggerated and misinterpreted, since present-day techniques of making such studies were not then available; and 2) that many of the traits blamed on inferior heredity were actually the result of *inferior environment*. This is not to say that the "Jukes" and "Kallikaks" may not have been more than ordinarily defective, or to deny that in some family groups genes for certain types of defects and abnormalities may collect and be passed on in above average proportions, just as in other family groups "superior" genes may be more prevalent. But as noted in previous chapters, we are still far from knowing what part, if any, heredity plays in such traits as alcoholism, criminality, "immorality," or "degeneracy," and if these traits are concentrated in certain families, we may have to assume—unless proved otherwise—that this is mostly because of the bad environment running in these families. (For detailed discussion of the "Kallikak" study and points involved see the author's article, "The Kallikaks After Thirty Years," *Journal of Heredity,* September, 1944; also pp. 525-530 in *"The New* You and Heredity.")

Racial ancestry. One frequently hears a person say, "I'm one-fourth Irish," or "I'm one thirty-second American Indian." In Nazi Germany many people were persecuted or exterminated because they were "one-eighth" Jewish. And in some parts of the United States the fact that a person is labeled "one-sixteenth" Negro, or less, is sufficient to bar him from White society and privileges. All such references to a person being precisely this or that fraction of a given ethnic group or race have little meaning genetically. The actual hereditary relationship of a person of mixed racial or ethnic descent to any of his ancestral groups depends entirely on the number of chromosomes of that group he carries; and it is impossible to do more than guess about this. For example, if a Mulatto (half Negro), married a "pure" White person, all their children would be considered, technically, "one-fourth" Negro. Each child having one and the same Negro grandparent, would, on the average, be assumed to carry twelve Negro chromosomes. But actually (as explained in a previous section) any given "one-fourth" Negro child could be carrying any proportion of the Negro grandparent's chromosomes. One child might be carrying many more than twelve, a brother or sister many fewer—to the point of having only one or two Negro chromosomes. Again it would be possible for a person who is technically "one-sixteenth" Negro to be carrying more Negro chromosomes than one who is technically "one-eighth" or even "one-fourth" Negro. Nor can anyone tell from a person's features, or from any known test, how many or how few Negro genes he is carrying. The genes that determine surface appearance are only a very small part of the total genes in a person, and these "feature" genes may work independently of most other genes. Thus, among offspring of Mulattoes, a child who looks most Negroid might actually be carrying fewer Negro genes than a child who looks most White. All of these facts apply equally to a person who had a grandparent, or other ancestor of any given racial or ethnic group—Chinese, Japanese, Indian or French, Irish, Jewish, etc.

RELATIVES: LEGAL AND HEREDITARY. Many of the facts about genetic relationships to ancestors apply to other kin

—brothers and sisters, aunts and uncles, cousins, etc. The hereditary relationship between any relatives, as with ancestors, depends entirely on how many of their chromosomes are the same, which can only be guessed at in terms of averages. The exceptions, other than parents (with each of whom one has twenty-four chromosomes in common), are identical twins, who provide our first example of legal and genetic differences with respect to relatives.

▶ *Identical twins and other siblings.* The law makes no distinction between 1) identical twins, or 2) fraternal twins, or ordinary brothers or sisters. Yet in the first case there is definite 100 per cent hereditary relationship—all of the forty-eight chromosomes in identical twins being the same—while in the other cases there is only an uncertain 50 per cent relationship. That is to say, non-identical children in a family may be carrying any combination of twenty-four chromosomes from each parent; and while on the average half of these may be the same in any two of these children, it is possible that the proportion may be more or less than half. Thus, of several children in a family, two might have not twenty-four, but thirty, thirty-two or more chromosomes in common, and be genetically much closer than either of them is to another child, who might have only eighteen, sixteen or fewer of the same chromosomes. Moreover, the degree of genetic relationship between any two children of the same parents cannot be proved merely by their similarity in surface traits, because genes in only a few of the chromosomes may be involved in producing these, and it is possible that two children who look less alike may be sharing more of the other chromosomes. In time geneticists believe, or hope, that there will be ways of knowing how many and which chromosomes of given parents the children are carrying.

▶ *The "sex-chromosome" relationship factor.* Certain slight (but sometimes important) differences in the genetic relationships of parents and children, brothers and sisters, result from the way the "X" and "Y" sex chromosomes are passed along. For instance, in quantity of genes, a son is at least 5 per cent more related to his mother than to his father. Reason: While of the twenty-four chromosomes a son receives from each parent, twenty-three are the same in the number of genes they carry, the additional X chromosome from his mother has many more genes than the small Y from his father—enough to bring the total genes from the mother to at least 5 per cent over those from the father. (This accounts for the many "sex-linked" diseases and defects which sons inherit solely through their mothers. See Chap. 11.) *Daughters,* since they receive an X chromosome from each parent, have genetically an exactly equal relationship to each.

Uncles, aunts, cousins. The general facts about chromosome relationships given for grandparents and ancestors apply to all other relatives. One can make only an estimate in terms of *averages,* as follows:

UNCLE ⎫
AUNT ⎭

Each is a one-fourth relative, with the average possibility of carrying replicas of twelve of one's forty-eight chromosomes. The relationship is the same as to a grandparent. (Your uncle, for instance if he is your father's brother, has an average of half his chromosomes in common with your father. And since you have half your father's chromosomes—or half of the uncle's half, one-half by one-half = one-fourth.)

GREAT-UNCLE ⎫
GREAT-AUNT ⎬
FIRST COUSIN ⎭

Each is a one-eighth relative, with the average possibility of carrying replicas of six of one's forty-eight chromosomes. The relationship is the same as to a great-grandparent. (Further discussions about "Cousins" in next chapter.)

GREAT-GRT. UNCLE ⎫
GREAT-GRT. AUNT ⎭

Each is a one-sixteenth relative, with the average possibility of carrying replicas of three of one's forty-eight chromosomes.

DISPUTED PARENTAGE CASES. The use of blood tests in many courts in the United States and Europe has already made it possible to clear more than half the men wrongly accused of fathering a child. The tests are even more effective in "interchanged-baby" cases, actual or alleged, when two sets of parents claim the same baby as their own. All of these parentage tests follow the same principle: Establishing the baby's inherited blood types in the different systems—A, B, O, Rh, M-N-S, etc.— and then finding out whether the man accused of being the father, or the couple claiming parentage, could have contributed these inherited factors. (See Chap. 15, Blood Types.) The tests *cannot prove* that a given man is the father of a given child, or that a particular couple are its parents, because there may be many other persons in the population with the required blood types. But the tests can rule out a man as the possible father, or a couple as the possible parents, if they show that he or they do not have one or another of the blood types needed for the child to be his or theirs.

▶ *"Exclusion" examples:* 1) A child's blood is O and a man's blood is AB. The man *cannot* be the child's father. 2) If the man does have O blood, a second test might follow, with the "MN" types: Should the baby have the "M" type, and the man the "N" type, this would exclude him. 3) If the man does have blood-type "M," the tests would go on to the "Rh" series, and again there might be a chance that the man did not carry the particular "Rh" gene which would have had to be transmitted by the child's father. Tests of the mother's blood are necessary to give the most complete results. For instance, if a baby's blood is AB, a man with A blood could have been the father. But if the mother's blood is also A, then the father must have been the one who gave the child the "B" gene, so the "A" man would be ruled out. Altogether, with the principal blood tests employed today (A, B, O, Rh, and M-N series), a man wrongly accused of parentage has about a 55 per cent chance of being cleared. This, however, is the average chance for a mixed American population, in which divergent proportions of the blood groups and blood types are represented. In a community or group here or abroad where most persons are of closely similar stock, and with small differences in blood types, the chance of parentage exclusion of any man would be greatly reduced. On the other hand, if a man has blood types which are infrequent in a given community or group, his chance of exclusion if wrongly accused of paternity might be very high. (See also Chap. 26, *Race differences in blood types.*)

▶ *"Changelings."* Despite the many precautions taken by hospitals today, there are some rare instances of babies being given to the wrong parents. Since two babies and two sets of parents are involved, blood tests usually can establish whether there has been any interchange. In addition, footprints, handprints and other traits of parents and children in which heredity plays a part can help to make the proof conclusive. (See also next section.)

"Feature clues" in parentage cases. Occasionally rare inherited physical traits in a child may provide a means of proving or disproving someone's parentage. If a child has any unusual *dominant* surface trait listed in previous chapters (Hapsburg jaw, drooping eyelids, any of various hand abnormalities, etc.) and the mother does not have this trait, its presence or absence in a man accused of paternity might be significant. In some cases, also, certain features or coloring, if their inheritance is clear-cut, might carry weight with respect to parentage. Obviously, if a baby has black hair, dusky skin and jet-black eyes, and the mother is a fair-skinned, blue-eyed blonde, a man who is also fair, light-haired and blue-eyed is hardly likely to be the child's father. However, one must be extremely cautious about forming judgments or suspicions regarding parentage on the basis of a few surface traits. Many hereditary traits do not show themselves or become set until late in childhood, or in the mature years, and thus have no value if decisions must be made regarding an infant's parentage. Further, the mere resemblance or lack of resemblance between a person and a given infant need not offer proof or disproof of parentage, since a child may sometimes be quite unlike either of its true parents in coloring and other feature details. (Chap. 6.) But taken altogether, a number of inherited feature traits could have a bearing on parentage cases where the blood tests are inconclusive.

29

Parenthood Problems

APPLIED GENETICS. Interesting as the subject of human genetics may be, its main importance lies in the practical contributions it can make to human welfare and happiness. True, the application of genetic principles has led to vast improvements in plant and animal breeding, with better quality and increased production of grains, fruits, vegetables, beef, poultry, milk and virtually every other major cultivated food product on today's tables. In antibiotics, applied genetics has greatly increased the production of penicillin, streptomycin and other disease-fighting organisms. But in these and many other ways, the achievements of genetics have come through working with *non-human* genes. What has been, or can be accomplished, by applying the principles of genetics directly to the improvement of human genes and human breeding? In this and the next chapter we will present some of the answers.

Uses of Human Genetics. At various points in this book it has been shown how the knowledge of human genetics has swept away many superstitions, false beliefs, fears, and harmful theories about heredity that have plagued people for ages; how it has helped to give parents and children a better insight into their biological relationships; how it has clarified the nature and causes of many diseases and defects and made possible better medical diagnoses and treatment; how such specific findings as those relating to the "Rh factor" have aided in saving the lives of thousands of babies; how with respect to traits of intelligence, achievement, talent, and behavior, we are now better able to identify the relative roles of heredity and environment, and deal more fairly and sensibly with individuals; and how the facts regarding race and ancestry are all working to promote better

242

understanding among human beings in general. Now we will take up some of the ways in which human genetic findings can guide persons in important individual situations.

PERSONAL HEREDITY PROBLEMS. The most common of these involve fear of inheritance or transmission of defects, diseases or other undesirable traits. In each case, once it is clear that a given condition *is* hereditary, decisions must be governed by its severity; the nature of its inheritance and the risk of transmission; the stage of life at which it appears; the degree of its interference with happiness, work or adjustment; and how prepared parents might be to have and rear a child so afflicted. Further, whether or not there is immediate danger of a defective child, socially minded persons might be concerned about passing on the defective gene to future generations. (See next chapter.) With respect to many of these points, the general answers can be found in preceding parts of this book. Where more specific guidance is needed, it may be obtained from various qualified persons, depending on the nature of the problem: If chiefly *medical,* from physicians specializing in the disease or defect; if chiefly *genetic,* from medical geneticists (see Appendix); if chiefly ethical, moral or social, from one's spiritual advisor or a qualified marriage counselor. Here are some of the situations for which advice is often sought:

▶ *1. A couple has had one seriously defective child.* Should they risk having another? One must first be sure about the nature of the condition. Many congenital abnormalities are purely environmental, due to prenatal accidents or the mother's temporary condition, and may not occur again. (The doctor in the case can best determine this.) If the condition is clearly hereditary, the chance of a repeat with another child may be great or small, depending on the method of inheritance, as shown in the accompanying table of "repeat threats." In any case one should not make the common error of thinking that "lightning doesn't strike twice," or that if the risk of having a defective child is one in four, for example, once one has appeared the next three will be normal. As with a dice number turning up, two or three genetically defective children may appear in succession. On the other hand, the risk of a repeat is often so small that a genetic

CHANCES OF A "REPEAT" DEFECTIVE CHILD
(Whether hereditary or not)

If a couple has had one child with this defect:	*The chances of having another child with the same defect are:*
Idiocy	
Mongolian	1 in 50
Amaurotic or phenylpyruvic	1 in 4
Cretinism	Uncertain
Hydrocephaly	1 in 60
Feeble-mindedness (IQ 50 to 70)	
If both parents normal	1 in 10
If one parent a moron	Up to 1 in 5
If both parents morons	Up to 3 in 4
Schizophrenia	Up to 1 in 12
Albinism	1 in 4
Clubfoot	1 in 30
Harelip (with or without cleft palate)	1 in 7
Spina bifida	1 in 25
Extra fingers and/or toes	1 in 2
Malformed hands or feet (hereditary types only, listed in Chap. 13)	Up to 1 in 2
Hip, congenital dislocation	1 in 30
Heart, malformed	1 in 50
Kidney, polycystic congenital	1 in 4
Intestines, pyloric stenosis	1 in 17
Any other hereditary defect or abnormality mentioned previously in this book:	
If recessive	1 in 4
If dominant	1 in 2

(Risks for either of the above are much reduced
where the condition is listed as "qualified.")

advisor may tell the parents not to hesitate too much about having more children.

▶ 2. *A couple who have not yet had children are hesitating about having any,* because one mate is afflicted with an extremely serious hereditary condition.

A. If the condition is a clear *dominant,* it will probably be transmitted to *one in two* children. With the risk so great most genetic advisors might counsel against having children. For "dominant-*qualified*" conditions the risks are smaller, but still ominous.

B. If the condition is *recessive,* there will be no defective child unless the other mate is carrying a gene for exactly the same defect. Clues as to whether this is so may come from that mate's family history, and in the case of some diseases, from tests. (See Chap. 11, "Forecasting Disease Inheritance.")

C. If the condition is *sex-linked* (usually with the gene on the X chromosome), and if the husband is afflicted, there will be no children with the defect, but there is a fifty-fifty threat for each of his daughter's sons. In some of the very serious sex-linked conditions (hemophilia, certain muscular atrophies, certain blindness conditions, etc.) there would be every reason for afflicted men not to have children.

▶ 3. *Both members of a couple have serious hereditary defects.* If these are *dominant,* the facts in 2(A) apply even more strongly. If the defects are *recessive,* the important point is whether they are exactly the same ones in both mates. If they are, *all* the children might be affected. But if the husband's and wife's hereditary afflictions are entirely different, *none* of the children might have either defect. However, every child would become a carrier of two defective genes.

▶ 4. *Neither member of a couple (married or contemplating marriage) is defective,* but serious hereditary defects have appeared in close relatives of each. Here again, the question is whether the defects on both sides are the same or not, and how they are inherited. If the defects are the same, and *recessive,* there is a chance both mates are carrying genes for it, and might produce a defective child (but with the risk no more than one in four). If the recessive defects are different (as, for instance, some form of hereditary blindness on one side, deafness on the other), no child would be likely to have *either* defect, since matching genes would be required from both parents. If the conditions running in both families are clearly *dominant,* the fact that both mates are free of the conditions would prove they are not carrying the defective genes, so there would be no threat to their children. However, in *dominant-qualified* conditions, or those with late onset, there cannot be the same certainty. (See Guide, end of Chap. 11.)

▶ 5. *A couple with all the children they expect, and none yet defective, are nevertheless concerned for the future because of hereditary defects in close relatives.* Is there reason for such concern, and does it help any to worry? Sometimes, yes, if the hereditary defects or diseases are among those whose appearance depends on environmental factors, or on age, or both. For instance, if childhood rheumatism, diabetes, cancer, mental diseases, allergies, etc., have appeared in families, there should be alertness to possible symptoms in the children, and special precautions should be taken if needed. Especially hopeful is the fact that as medical science has been tracking down the causes of various hereditary defects and diseases, and linking some of them with abnormalities or upsets in the body chemistry, the chances of reducing their seriousness through early detection and treatment is increasing.

▶ 6. *A young man and woman, much in love, are hesitating about marriage because of certain bad traits in relatives of one or the other*—criminality, drunkenness, sexual abnormality, etc.— which they fear might crop up in their children. As we saw in previous chapters, there is little evidence that such behavior traits are hereditary, and even if they were, their transmission would be so complex that a child would run virtually no chance of "inheriting" these tendencies of a grandfather, uncle or aunt. Nothing in the situation as stated should prevent a marriage; in fact, if the man and woman are themselves normal, of good character and well-adjusted, any genetic risks would be outweighed by the advantages they bring to a marriage.

COUSIN MARRIAGES. Popular fears that cousin, or near-relative, marriages may result in seriously defective offspring have a basis in fact, although the threats are often not as great as many imagine. The risk in these marriages can be simply explained: When a husband and wife are closely related, they have a much greater than average chance of carrying the same genes; and if any of these genes are bad ones—particularly serious hidden recessives—there is a much above average chance that a child will receive a double dose of the same "black" gene, and be defective. For example, *first cousins* are alike in *one eighth* of their genes, on the average. (Chap. 28.) Should one of them, even though completely normal, be carrying a gene for any recessive defect (idiocy, albinism, hereditary blindness or deafness, etc.) the other cousin would have a one-in-eight chance of carrying a matching gene; and if this were actually the case, there would be a one-in-four chance of having a child with the defect. But if one cousin is himself (or herself) afflicted with a recessive defect—which means carrying two of the genes for it—the chance of the same gene being present in a first-cousin mate is *one in four,* and if it is present there is a fifty-fifty threat of their having a defective child. In any other conditions requiring certain genes from both parents, the genetic risks for offspring of first-cousin marriages are much above average. Moreover, while the rarity of a condition decreases the probability that two unrelated parents will both be carrying the gene for it, in the case of first cousins, once one carries a given gene, the chance that the other also carries it is always the same, regardless of the condition. In marriages of *second cousins,* with one in thirty-two genes in common, and third cousins, with one in 128 genes in common, the risk of their having defective children is naturally much smaller than with first cousins, but is still far above the average for non-related persons.

▶ *Evidence.* In groups where there has been much inbreeding, the incidence of certain hereditary defects is often unusually high, if there were defective genes in these groups to begin with. This has been found true in some isolated rural communities in the United States (Martha's Vineyard, Chesapeake Bay peninsulas, Kentucky mountains) and in some sections of Switzerland, Sweden, Japan and other countries, where the cousin-marriage rate has reached close to 10 per cent. In these groups there are much above average incidences of one hereditary defect or another, including feeble-mindedness, deafness, albinism, and dwarfism. Equally true, in many other groups, the rarer a recessive defect, the more one is apt to find that afflicted persons are offspring of marriages between relatives. In *albinos,* close to one in five have parents who were first cousins, and in some rarer conditions the ratio may reach even higher. In amaurotic idiocy about one in six or seven cases stem from first-cousin marriages, and many other cases would show marriages between relatives further back. However, in all groups and most countries the proportion of defectives with cousin parents has been decreasing as the incidence of cousin marriages has steadily declined. Reasons: Increasing movements of people, which are breaking up close-knit groups; greater opportunity for young people to go afield for their mates; and decrease in family sizes, which has cut down the number of cousins available for marriage. In the

Cousin Marriages

FIRST-COUSIN MATES **OFFSPRING**

One eighth of the genes of first cousins are the same. If one cousin carries a hidden (recessive) bad gene, the chance is one in eight the other has the same gene.

If first cousins marry, the risk is thus much above average that a child will receive two of the same bad genes, and will develop the recessive defect.

United States and most modern countries first-cousin marriages
are now much under one per cent (except in some rural areas),
and eventually may occur not oftener than one in three hundred
times, or less. (Laws against first-cousin marriages in twenty-
eight states of the United States may also have been a factor in
decreasing their incidence.)

▶ *Fairly "safe" or desirable cousin marriages.* Where there is
a reasonable assurance that no serious hereditary defect has appeared in their mutual family line for some generations, the
genetic risk in marriages between cousins may be relatively
small. Thus, there is little evidence that extensive inbreeding
among the Puritans, the ancient Spartans, or more recently, the
Pitcairn Islanders—the highly inbred descendants of the famed
mutineers of the *Bounty*—had any especially harmful effects.
In families of unusually sound stock and superior qualities,
cousin marriages may even tend to produce superior children.
That is to say, where there are concentrations of certain superior
genes (as for high intelligence, musical talent, artistry, or good
qualities of various kinds), marriages between cousins will increase the chances that desired gene-combinations will be passed
on to offspring. In some families, therefore, the possible good
results might offset the risks. One might note that Charles Darwin was married to his first cousin, Emma Wedgwood (of the
famed china makers), and had many distinguished descendants.
Abraham Lincoln was also the product of a cousin marriage. In
the Bible one finds many examples of close-relative marriages
with notable descendants: Jacob, married to his first cousins,
Rachel and Leah; Abraham married to his half sister; and Amram married to his aunt, and siring Moses, Aaron and the
prophetess Miriam. In the royal families of ancient Egypt marriages between brothers and sisters were the rule for generations
(Cleopatra having descended from six generations of such marriages), and apparently were not harmful to offspring. All of
this, incidentally, would show that there is no "natural instinct"
against incest among human beings (any more than in lower
animals) but that such prohibitions against near-relative marriages which are found in taboos, laws or religious proscriptions,

usually arose from social, psychological, or assumed genetic reasons.

ADOPTIONS. Fears of hereditary risks may apply not only to people's own children, but to children whom they might want to adopt. In former times the fears regarding hereditary traits in children of unknown or uncertain parentage who were offered for adoption tended to be grossly exaggerated. Today, many of these old fears have been greatly lessened as the demand for babies to adopt, in the United States particularly, is vastly exceeding the supply. If there is a genetic risk in an adopted baby, it is recognized that every child of one's own is also a genetic gamble to some extent. One offsetting advantage in the case of babies offered for adoption is that prospective foster parents can at least make sure that there are no obvious defects to begin with. Reputable adoption agencies also report any risks that the baby may present, and permit its return if any serious inborn defect shows itself in the near future. (Usually there is a probationary period of six months or more for both child and foster parents.) With respect to the ultimate "character" of an adopted child, there is a tendency now to believe that it will be determined much less by the behavior traits of the true parents than by those of the foster parents, and by the environment and training they provide.

30

Eugenics

HUMAN INEQUALITY. When governments and religions avow that "All men are created equal," it is recognized that this refers to the rights of all human beings under the laws of God and man to be given fair and equal treatment. No one can be unaware that Nature does not follow this principle in fashioning people's minds and bodies, but brings individuals into the world with many inequalities in their inherent makeup and chances for survival, achievement and happiness. This fact has been a troubling one throughout history, and has given rise to various notions, practices and plans. In some groups, such as the Spartans, defective offspring were killed (as they still are among various primitive peoples). Other groups have assumed that they could grade themselves into "superior" and "inferior" hereditary classes, born and bred for different roles and stations in life. Still others have felt that their own racial or ethnic group was inherently destined to dominate—and if they wished, to exterminate—"inferior" peoples (the latest example having been the Nazis). Beyond this the thought has always persisted that, inasmuch as human beings could successfully breed lower animals for improved and special qualities, why could they not control their own breeding toward more desirable goals? Some of the many problems raised by this question will be dealt with now.

"EUGENICS." This term, derived from the Greek *eugenes* ("well-born"), refers to measures for improving the hereditary makeup of the human species. Eugenics is not a science, and should not be confused with "genetics" (as it often is), although as advocated today it draws on genetic principles. However, when the eugenics movement was launched and named by Sir Francis Galton, in England in 1883, the science of genetics had not yet come into being. Thus, at the beginning, the eugenics program was based on many wrong beliefs regarding the inheritance of various traits, the division of people into inborn "superior" and "inferior" stocks or classes, and the manner in which "unfit" individuals could be quickly bred out of the human species and a race of "supermen" produced. Because of the extreme attitudes and proposals of many early "eugenists," and their failure to distinguish between the effects of bad heredity and bad environment, their movement met with much opposition. In recent years this has changed considerably, as the eugenics proposals have become sounder, more conservative and better adapted to new scientific facts and social changes. Thus present-day eugenics advocates have come to include many respected geneticists, social scientists and population experts.

Modern eugenic problems. What has concerned many authorities has been a lopsided trend in the childbearing situation: On the average, parents who are most "fit"—those most educated (and perhaps also most intelligent), successful, healthy, socially advanced and able to do most for their families—tend to have proportionately the fewest offspring. At the other extreme, parents considered less "fit"—the least educated (and often least intelligent), least successful, living in unfavorable environments and able to do least for their families—tend to have the most children. This is a reversal of the situation in former times, when the most "fit" and successful families, living as they did under the best conditions, had the most children. The chief reason for the change, of course, is that in the groups which today are most advanced, childbearing is voluntarily limited to a much greater extent than in the less advanced groups.

▶ *Group IQ differences.* The important eugenic question is whether the parents producing the most children today, on the average, are genetically inferior, particularly in mental ability, to those producing fewer children. If so, mankind's hereditary qualities would be deteriorating. But there is no clear evidence on this point—only deductions from a few facts. As noted in Chapter 19, IQs of children tend to follow the levels of their fathers' positions, being highest for children of professional men and executives, and grading down to lowest for children of unskilled workers. But here there is question of how far IQs (except among defectives) actually measure or reflect differences in inherited basic intelligence. Many would maintain that IQ tests are so much slanted toward educational factors that the lower IQs of the socially backward large-family groups are due to their inferior opportunities. Others maintain that making full allowances for environmental effects, the genetically superior persons would have been more likely to have risen to the top in any group, and that the high IQs of the more advanced and successful individuals, and of their children, do on the average reflect higher levels of inherited intelligence. On this basis, since the higher IQ groups have been producing fewer children and the lower IQ groups proportionately more, it has been claimed that the general level of basic intelligence in countries such as England and the United States has dropped several points in the past few generations. (This assumption cannot be considered proved.)

▶ *Recent changes in birth rates.* Whatever the facts might previously have been, recent social, educational and economic advances have made the birth-rate picture less extreme. There has been a considerable increase in childbearing in the more "fit" and educated groups, particularly in the United States; women college graduates, of whom a very large percentage used to remain spinsters, are now marrying and having children almost up to the general average; and more and more professional women are combining careers with motherhood. At the same time an increasing proportion of parents from the former backward ranks have been upgraded into the "fit" ranks; there has been a decrease in the birth rates of groups formerly considered less "fit" or advanced, as the birth-control practice has spread; and the placing of proportionately more mental defectives in institutions has withdrawn them from the ranks of possible parents. (Sterilization of defectives will be discussed later.) Nevertheless, there continues to be enough difference in the undesirable aspects of the birth-rate and genetic picture to make many authorities feel that certain measures should be taken. These are of two types, "positive eugenics," to increase the numbers of "fit" individuals, and "negative eugenics," to decrease the numbers of the "unfit," in all groups.

NEGATIVE EUGENICS. This involves all measures which, theoretically, could prevent or reduce the births of "unfit" individuals—those so defective that they would be a burden to their families, a detriment to the world, and would themselves find no happiness in being born. The measures proposed would leave the prevention of such births almost entirely to voluntary action by the potential parents (except in the case of those mentally unable to decide for themselves). Not only hereditary, but environmental threats would be considered. Whatever the cause, couples who are low-grade morons, or insane, or criminal or degenerate, are not likely to be "fit" parents, and limiting their reproduction might be good for society. However, some of the eugenic steps proposed to combat this are highly controversial. Particularly, there has been certain religious opposition. In discussing some of the suggested "negative eugenic" measures we are not necessarily recommending them.

▶ "*Birth control.*" The preceding chapter presented various genetic situations in which persons might feel justified in not having children, or not having more than those already born. Opposition to preventing or limiting reproduction in these cases, it should be clear, is *not to the principle* involved, but to the means. For instance, Roman Catholic authorities have stated that where there are strong probabilities that a genetically defective child will be produced, avoidance of conception may be justified; and where parents have as many children as they can hope to educate, rear healthily, and provide for suitably, or as the mother can bear without overtaxing her strength, limitation of reproduction is sanctioned. (Statement by Pope Pius XII in November, 1951.) The Catholic opposition is to control of conception by "*artificial*"—mechanical or chemical—*means*. What is permitted is only "natural" control, either by abstinence from sexual relations or confining them to the so-called "safe period" in the woman's menstrual cycle. The latter, or "rhythm" method, however, while able to reduce considerably the chances of conception, is often unreliable and ineffective, since a woman's fertile period cannot always be established with certainty. It might be noted that there is no formal religious opposition to birth-control methods among the great majority of Protestants and

Jews (except for a few sects in each), nor among most Hindus, Buddhists or Mohammedans. In a number of Asiatic countries (India, Japan) government programs of birth control are already under way, primarily to keep the population from growing out of bounds.

Sterilization. This is the most extreme method of birth control: An operation which permanently prevents reproduction. In a woman the fallopian tubes, which deliver eggs to the womb, are cut and tied; in a man the tubes which carry sperms from the testes are likewise cut and tied. (Neither operation has any effect on a person's desire or capacity for sexual performance.) Such operations are legally authorized in twenty-seven American states (although not carried out in all), and in some European countries (mainly Scandinavian), in cases of individuals who are mentally defective or insane and are likely to produce mentally defective offspring. Sterilizations also are authorized in a limited number of other cases, involving serious hereditary defects, and in some states (chiefly California and Indiana) for habitual criminals, habitual sexual offenders and "degenerates." (The latter sterilizations are chiefly for social reasons, since there is no proof that such persons are products of defective heredity.) Altogether, from 1907, when the first American sterilization law became effective (in Indiana) until January, 1955, 57,218 legal eugenic sterilizations were performed in the United States, 34,282 on women, 22,936 on men. Of these, about half were for mental deficiency, 44 per cent for insanity, the rest for other causes. In addition, it is estimated there have been from one thousand to two thousand private sterilization operations annually in the United States, some on individuals who feared they might transmit serious hereditary defects, and some on women whose lives would have been threatened by childbearing (as in certain cases of nephritis, heart disease, etc.).

▶ *What can sterilization accomplish?* Initial hopes that many of the worst hereditary defects could be quickly and easily wiped out by sterilizing the afflicted persons, have been much deflated by these findings:

1. The most common of the serious hereditary defects are *recessive* or otherwise due to multiple genes, which means that

persons who are themselves afflicted are only a small proportion of those carrying the genes. For instance, for every hundred thousand hereditary morons, there might be a million persons carrying single "moron" genes. Thus, sterilizing all those with recessive or multiple-gene defects would not prevent most of the genes involved from being passed on, so the proportion of defectives in future generations would be only slightly reduced.

2. In *sex-linked* defects we again have the problem of the carriers. Most of these conditions afflict only or chiefly males (Chap. 11). But sterilizing these defective males would still leave the biggest proportion of the genes to be transmitted by female carriers. While one can tell when a woman is such a carrier if her father has or had the sex-linked condition, or if she has had an afflicted son, sterilization might be justified only in extreme and rare cases. (Hemophilia, or some sex-linked muscular, eye and mental defects.)

3. *Dominant* hereditary defects, caused directly by a single gene, could be greatly reduced in incidence by sterilizing those affected. But the serious dominant conditions are rare. Moreover, new gene mutations usually keep replenishing these defects, so they might never be completely wiped out. Also difficult to eradicate would be the "qualified" or partly dominant genes, whose effects may "skip" the parent but crop out in a child, and genes for conditions with late onset which may not appear in a parent until after the children are born.

▶ *Objections to sterilization programs.* One reason for the present "go slow" attitude toward sterilization is the fear that it might get out of hand. This was shockingly shown during the Nazi terror reign, when hundreds of thousands of persons were sterilized on the flimsiest eugenic grounds, or merely because they were of political, racial, ethnic or religious groups of whom the Nazis disapproved. Other reasons: 1) The growing possibility that treatments will be found to reduce the threats of many hereditary defects (as has happened with diabetes). 2) The fact that some persons who are genetically defective in one way (blindness, deafness, muscular afflictions, etc.) may be genetically superior in other ways. 3) Religious opposition. However, should means be found to produce sterilization temporarily, or only for as long as desired, many of the objections to it might be lessened or eliminated. (Progress in developing a "contraceptive pill" has been reported at this writing.)

POSITIVE EUGENICS. This refers to any measures which could lead to the improvement of the human stock by increasing the proportion of healthy, intelligent, capable and useful persons. Some of the recommended steps, as noted before, already are being carried out through economic and social advances in the United States and other countries. Earlier marriages and earlier childbearing, when mothers are healthiest, are producing more children and healthier children in the "fit" groups. Better prenatal and child care, and vastly improved medical treatments, are reducing the proportions of defectives in all groups. Increased income for young persons, subsidies from parents, hospitalization plans, unemployment benefits, social security, etc., are easing worries about having and rearing children among those who want them most and can do most for them. All of these steps were once basic planks in the positive eugenics platform.

▶ *Sterility treatments.* As part of the program of helping "fit" persons to become parents, great progress has been made in overcoming many cases of sterility and bringing children to previously barren couples. (For information regarding "sterility" clinics, see Appendix.) In up to one in three sterility cases the cause may lie in the husband's failure to produce fertile sperms, or sufficient sperms, which need not be related to disease, health and/or virility. Where the wife has been barren it may be because of her inability to produce fertile eggs, or if she does conceive, to carry a child through to birth. In close to a third of the sterility cases the difficulties can be overcome.

Artificial insemination. This is a controversial process which has been employed in recent years in some cases where the wife is fertile but the husband is sterile, and the sperms of another man are used to conceive a baby. (In occasional instances the method is resorted to if there would be hereditary risks in the husband's fathering the child.) One might note first that artificial insemination is now widespread in livestock breeding, perhaps 15 per cent of all dairy cows in the United States, and many race horses, being bred by this method. In the case of humans the procedure began to be used several decades ago, and since then perhaps forty thousand babies have been conceived in the United States in this way.

▶ *The technical procedure.* In all artificial insemination cases the first requirement is that the husband must consent and will accept the resulting child as his own. With this provision, a qualified medical expert then obtains fertile sperms from another man and injects them into the wife. From a purely physical standpoint the method has proved effective and satisfactory. The "donors" whose sperms are used are carefully selected, being mostly young college men of good health, character and hereditary background. In each case the "donor," or proxy father (whose identity is kept secret by the doctor), is "matched" as nearly as possible with the husband's coloring, appearance, racial stock and blood groups. The wife is then inseminated at her most fertile time, and when she is in the best state for motherhood.

▶ *Objections to the method.* It is estimated that at least one million couples in the United States are childless because of the husband's sterility, and could have children if they utilized the artificial-insemination method. The fact that only an extremely small proportion do (from two to three thousand annually), can be ascribed to these reasons: 1) *Psychological*—most often the husband's antagonism to the procedure. However, once the initial objections are overcome, only a small fraction of the artificial-insemination cases have led to any marital conflict. 2) *Religious.* Artificial insemination with other than a husband's sperm was condemned as "illicit and immoral" by Pope Pius XII in 1949, and was also opposed by the British Archbishop of Canterbury in the same year. However, many Protestant authorities have approved the method when it helps to bring children to otherwise childless couples. No formal opposition has come from Jewish sources. 3) *Legal problems.* Many complex legal aspects of artificial insemination (when the sperm used is not the husband's) remain to be settled. In the very few instances that courts have so far dealt with the problems raised, conflicting opinions have been given. A New York judge held in 1948 that an artificial-insemination baby is not illegitimate. A Chicago judge ruled contrariwise in 1954. The case was appealed and is awaiting final decision at this writing.

Future possibilities: *Sperm preservation.* The possibility that by the quick-freezing process human sperms may be stored for long periods, and that "semen banks" may become available for inseminations, is held out by recent experiments. At the State University of Iowa in 1954 it was reported that already four recently born babies had been conceived through inseminations with previously frozen and stored sperms. If such storage can be continued successfully for years, it may bring to reality the theory that in some future time the sperms of a great man may be used to sire hundreds of children long after his death.

▶ *"Proxy" mothers.* In line with the preceding statement, there is also the fantastic possibility that some women in the near future may be able to have children *without bearing them:* by transplanting the fertilized egg from one woman to the womb of another, who will then mother the fetus through to birth. Experimentally, this transplanting of eggs (and sometimes whole ovaries) has already been carried out in lower animals (cows, dogs, rabbits and mice). In all of these cases, it is important to note, the offspring, in their hereditary traits, were *as much like the mother from whose egg they developed as they would have been had they grown in her own womb,* and in no way developed traits of the "proxy" mother. Back of these lower-animal experiments is the thought that eventually any prize or thoroughbred female—horse, cow, dog, etc.—will be enabled to produce many more offspring than she could alone in the normal way, by having various other females "mother" her eggs. With respect to human beings the process of employing "proxy" mothers may have great value some day for women who can produce fertile eggs and conceive, but are unable to carry children through to birth because of uterine deficiencies, or for whom motherhood would be dangerous because of certain diseases (nephritis, heart ailments, etc.).

BREEDING "SUPERIOR" HUMANS. Growing out of some of the remarkable breeding techniques now successfully used with lower animals may be the thought that they could also be used to produce more and better *"human* thoroughbreds." The idea is appealing. *But*—who is to decide what types of human beings we should breed for? Lower animals are bred for only a few specific traits; one is not concerned with the other traits. A horse may be a speedy racer, but no good for heavy work. Or a dog may have a fine-shaped head and body, but be quite unintelligent. A desirable and successful human being, however, must have a great many unique qualities, each of them highly complex and dependent on a great many genes. We have seen how difficult it would be merely to breed out serious defects— even those produced by a few simple genes. There would be far more difficulty in trying to *breed in* almost any of the "desirable" traits—superior minds, great talents, fine characters—the complex genes for which have not even been discovered. Most difficult of all would be trying to combine in one stock of humans not merely these traits, but also beauty, strong physique and superb health. Finally, when we consider that thoroughbred cattle, horses, and dogs are the products of hundreds of generations of selective breeding—and that a generation for these lower animals is a fraction of a human generation—any extensive plan to breed "superior" human beings must seem remote, if not also dangerous.

Mankind's future. In this atomic age, the power of human beings to destroy themselves or warp their genes is clearly much greater and more imminent than their power to improve themselves and their genes. There is little question then, that the immediate hope for human happiness lies primarily in making the most of what genes we already have, and of the power they carry to change and improve our environment. This power that lies in the human gene is vastly greater than that which lies in the atom. We can explode the atom and cause destruction. We can develop and utilize the power within the gene to do untold constructive good. As we learn to understand our genes, we will also learn to better understand ourselves and our fellow men, and how to manage our lives for the greatest benefit to all. In the end, human beings can never be more than their genes permit them to be. They should strive not to be less.

Appendix

GLOSSARY

*Terms not defined in this book, but which the reader
may encounter in other books or in technical articles
dealing with human heredity.*

Agglutination. Clumping in the blood when there is a transfusion involving persons of conflicting blood types.

Agglutinin. The substance, or "antibody," in the blood serum of a person which causes the afore-mentioned clumping of the red blood cells of another person.

Agglutinogen. The substance, or "antigen," in the red blood cells of a person which is affected by the conflicting agglutinin of another person.

Alleles; Allelomorphs. Referring to genes which are assigned to the same function, and are usually located in the same place in matching chromosomes, but which do not necessarily work in the same way. As a gene for blue eyes from one parent, which is the "allele" of the eye-color gene received from the other parent.

Atavism. Reappearance of some trait of a remote ancestor in a person none of whose parents or grandparents show the trait.

Autosome. Any one of the chromosomes other than the sex chromosomes.

Chromatin. The substance in the chromosomes which shows up under the microscope after a cell is stained.

Chromomeres. The "beads" which are seen in a stained chromosome in its stretched-out stage, and which are believed to contain the genes (one gene, or perhaps several, to a bead).

Consanguinity. A close relationship in "blood," or heredity, as between cousins or other near relatives.

Cytoplasm. All the living material in the cell which is outside of the nucleus.

Diploid ("duplex"). With two sets of chromosomes. In human beings a fertilized egg, with forty-eight chromosomes, or twenty-four pairs, is in the "diploid" state. All the resulting body cells are also diploid. (See also "Haploid.")

Dizygotic. From two separate fertilized eggs, as in the case of fraternal twins. "Zygote" refers to the combination of a sperm and an unfertilized egg. (See also "Monozygotic.")

Dysgenic. Opposite of "eugenic." Tending to cause a deterioration in people through adverse breeding.

Epistasis. The covering up, or "masking" of the effects of a gene by an "outsider" gene which is not one of its alleles. (See "Allele.")

"F." The generation of offspring. The children of a given couple are referred to as "F-1." The grandchildren are "F-2," great-grandchildren, "F-3."

Gamete. A mature germ cell, either a sperm or an egg.

Genetic drift. A gradual change in the proportion of given genes within an isolated group of people which results mainly through the chance fact that persons with some genes may produce more offspring than persons with other genes. Thus, although originally two genetic traits may have been equally prevalent, in the course of generations persons with the one trait may become more numerous than those with the other trait, apart from any mutations or any deliberate selective breeding which may have occurred.

Genotype. The genetic makeup of individuals. Persons with the same genes have the same "genotype." When persons merely show the same physical traits, they are referred to as having the same "*phenotype.*" Sometimes persons with the same "genotype" may differ in "phenotype," as with identical twins who have developed differently because of environmental influences. Conversely, persons with the same "phenotype," showing the same physical traits, may or may not be carrying the same genes, as with two dark-eyed persons, one of whom carries two "dark-eye" genes, the other one "dark-eye" gene coupled with a hidden "light-eye" gene.

Germ plasm. The material of the germ cells, in the testes of the male or the ovaries of the female, from which sperms or eggs with their chromosomes are fashioned.

Gonad. A reproductive gland: Testicle in the male, ovary in the female.

Haploid. With a single set of chromosomes. In human beings each sperm or egg is a "haploid" cell, containing only one set, or twenty-four single chromosomes, in contrast to a "diploid" cell, with two sets, as previously defined.

Hardy-Weinberg law. Referring to the principle by which a certain balance is maintained in a population with respect to the proportions of persons carrying a single hidden recessive gene for any trait, those carrying two of the genes, and showing the trait, and those free of the genes, and for estimating the ratios of all these individuals. Thus, if the number of persons with a recessive defect, such as albinism, is known, it is possible to estimate how many normal persons are carrying a hidden gene for the condition.

Heterosis. "Hybrid vigor": The improvement in vigor, size or other qualities which sometimes comes through crossbreeding individuals of different genetic stocks. (See text, Chap. 27, under "*Race mixing*.")

Heterozygote. A fertilized egg in which paired genes differ, because of different contributions from the two parents. A person who is "heterozygous" for eye color would be carrying two different eye-color genes, as, for instance one "blue-eye" gene and one "brown-eye" gene. In a person who is "homozygous" the two eye-color genes would be the same.

Holandric inheritance. Referring to the very rare cases in which a dominant gene is in the Y chromosome, with no equivalent gene in the X chromosome. Such a gene and the trait it produces would be passed along by an affected father to all of his sons, but would not occur in females.

Homologous chromosomes. Paired chromosomes with matching genes, one of the pair from the father, one from the mother. (See Illustration, Chap. 3.)

Homozygote. A fertilized egg in which given paired genes are the same. (See also "Heterozygote.")

Intersexes. In-between sexed individuals, with biological sex characteristics of both males and females.

Linkage. Referring to the connection of genes in the same chromosome. Linked genes are sometimes separated through chromosome crossovers. (See Illustration, Chap. 28.)

Locus. The location of a gene on a particular chromosome.

Meiosis. The process whereby a germ cell with two sets of chromosomes gives rise to sperms, or eggs, each with only one set of chromosomes.

Mitosis. The process whereby cells in the developing embryo divide and multiply, each cell forming two daughter cells with replicas of all the original chromosomes. (A simple aid in remembering the difference between "meiosis" and "mitosis": Think of "mei-O-" as "mei-*One*"—forming a cell [sperm or egg] with *one* set of chromosomes; "mitosis" as "mi-*Two*"—forming *two* cells, with two sets of chromosomes in each.)

Monozygotic. From a single fertilized egg, as in the case of identical twins. (See also "Dizygotic.")

Mutagen. Any force or influence—radiation, a chemical or other factor—which can cause mutations to occur in genes.

Pangenesis. An erroneous early theory advanced by Darwin, that each cell of the body gives off little particles, or "pangenes," embodying the cell's characteristics (whether acquired or inherited), and that these "pangenes" then find their way into the eggs or sperms and determine an offspring's heredity.

Parthenogenesis. Biological "virgin birth": The development of an individual from an unfertilized egg. This is normal in some lower animal (invertebrate) species, but is not known to occur naturally in mammals (except perhaps, theoretically, in the rarest of instances), although it has been artificially caused to happen in experiments with rabbits.

Proband. The person whose condition leads a geneticist (or other investigator) to begin research into the family history.

Propositus. The person from whom a line of descent is reckoned. Sometimes also used as a synonym for "proband." (See above.)

Somatic. Referring to all cells in the body ("soma") outside of the germ cells.

Spermatogenesis. The process by which sperms are produced.

Telegony. Referring to an old and false belief that if a female is mated to two different males, characteristics of the first male may carry along in her and be impressed on offspring sired by the second male, or succeeding males.

SUGGESTIONS FOR FURTHER READING

(For more detailed information regarding most aspects of human heredity and subjects dealt with in this handbook, as well as a fairly extensive list of references, the reader might turn first to the author's earlier, comprehensive work, "*The New* You and Heredity," published by J. B. Lippincott Co., Philadelphia, 1950. Additional details and references with special attention to disease inheritance and genetic techniques, will be found in the books listed below, except for "Women and Men," which concentrates on sex differences.)

Reference Books and Textbooks

Clinical Genetics. Edited by Arnold Sorsby. Butterworth & Co., London, 1953. An authoritative, technical compilation of articles on all important hereditary diseases and defects, by specialists in the respective fields of medical genetics. Chiefly for medical men and geneticists.

Human Genetics. (2 *vols.*) R. R. Gates. Macmillan, New York, 1946. Highly technical, with detailed attention to medical genetics, and extensive bibliographies. Some of the conclusions are debatable. Primarily for specialists.

Human Heredity. James V. Neel and William J. Schull. University of Chicago Press, 1954. An excellent textbook for advanced students of human genetics, biology and medicine. Detailed attention to mathematical aspects of human genetics.

Principles of Human Genetics. Curt Stern. W. H. Freeman & Co., San Francisco, 1949. Another excellent textbook for students of human genetics. Not too technical, for the most part, and broad in treatment.

Genetics and the Races of Man. William C. Boyd. Little, Brown & Co., Boston, 1950. Semi-popular, and with special emphasis on the blood groups from the anthropological viewpoint.

Heredity in Health and Mental Disorder. Franz J. Kallmann. W. W. Norton & Co., New York, 1953. Special emphasis on twin studies with respect to mental diseases and defects, and longevity.

Women and Men. Amram Scheinfeld. Harcourt, Brace & Co., New York, 1944. Popularly written; dealing in detail with the differences between the sexes—biological, social and psychological—and their development and significance.

Periodicals Dealing With Human Heredity

(Most of these are technical, and unless otherwise specified are recommended mainly to professional readers.)

Acta Geneticae Medicae et Gemellologiae. (Quarterly, published in Rome, Italy, but with many articles in English, or if not, with English summaries.) Special attention to new researches on twins.

American Journal of Human Genetics. (Quarterly. The official publication of the American Society of Human Genetics.) Mainly technical, but occasional semi-popular articles.

Annals of Human Genetics. (Quarterly, formerly *Annals of Eugenics.* Published in England.)

Eugenics Quarterly. (Published by the American Eugenics Society, New York.) Popularly written articles, by specialists on various aspects of human heredity, with special attention to problems of eugenics.

Human Biology. (Quarterly, published by Wayne University Press, Detroit, Mich.)

Journal of Heredity. (Bi-monthly, published by American Genetic Association, Washington, D.C.) Frequent articles on human genetics, chiefly technical, but some semi-popular.

Statistical Bulletin, Metropolitan Life Insurance Co., New York. (Monthly.) Latest reports on longevity and mortality rates for given diseases, by age and sex, with frequent attention to genetic aspects. Popularly written.

See also, for summaries of continuing research and findings on various aspects of human heredity:

—*Biological Abstracts.* (Monthly, published at the University of Pennsylvania.) Look under monthly headings, "Human Genetics," "Physical Anthropology" and "Human Biology," and consult annual indexes for special subjects.

—*Psychological Abstracts.* (Bi-monthly, published by the American Psychological Association, at Washington, D.C.) Occasional references to human heredity, particularly with respect to intelligence, personality, behavior deviations, speech disorders, color vision, etc. See subdivisions in separate issues, and consult annual index for special topics.

WHERE TO GET ADVICE

HUMAN HEREDITY CLINICS

Authoritative information and advice on problems of human heredity may be obtained at the following institutions. In most cases, however, if the person applying is a layman, it is advisable that contact be made first through one's physician, particularly if the problem is a medical one. *Where not otherwise specified, address inquiries to "Dept. of Human Genetics," at any of these institutions:*

Bowman Gray School of Medicine, Winston-Salem, N. C.
University of Chicago, Dept. of Zoology, Chicago, Ill.
Dight Institute, University of Minnesota, Minneapolis 14, Minn.
University of Michigan, Ann Arbor, Mich.
New York State Psychiatric Institute, New York 32, N. Y.
Ohio State University, Columbus, Ohio.

University of Oklahoma, Norman, Okla.
University of Texas, Austin, Tex.
Tulane University Medical School, New Orleans, La.
University of Utah, Salt Lake City, Utah.
Medical College of Virginia, Richmond, Va.

Canada:

Hospital for Sick Children, Toronto 2, Canada.
McGill University, Toronto, Canada.
Children's Memorial Hospital, Montreal, Canada.

INFERTILITY CLINICS

For couples concerned about the failure of the wife to conceive, information regarding clinics or private physicians specializing in the treatment of infertility may be obtained from the Planned Parenthood Federation of America, 501 Madison Avenue, New York 22, New York. Such infertility services are now available almost everywhere in the United States. In many cities the Federation operates its own infertility clinics, and in these cases couples can go directly to them. (Look first in your local telephone directory under "Planned Parenthood.")

Other countries: Planned Parenthood clinics also are now operating in Australia, Great Britain, Holland, India, Japan, Singapore, Sweden, Union of South Africa and Western Germany.

WHERE TO STUDY

Special courses in Human Genetics or Medical Genetics, or both, are given in all of the institutions listed under "Human Heredity Clinics" above, (except the two Canadian hospitals), and in addition at: Dartmouth College, Hanover, N. H.; Michigan State College, East Lansing, Mich.; College of the Ozarks, Clarkesville, Ark.; University of Rochester, Rochester, N. Y.; University of Toledo, Toledo, Ohio; Western Reserve University, Cleveland, Ohio; Johns Hopkins University, Baltimore, Md.; Columbia University, Institute for Study of Human Variations, New York City.

Other countries: Counseling in medical genetics is also given at institutions in Denmark, England, France, Germany, Holland, India, Italy, Japan, Norway, Sweden and Switzerland. For addresses write to the American Eugenics Society, 230 Park Avenue, New York 17, New York.

Index

14651